TO HAVE AND TO HOLD

By the same author:

To still the child (1992)

TO HAVE AND TO HOLD

Nicky Singer

Constable · London

First published in Great Britain 1993
by Constable and Company Limited
3 The Lanchesters, 162 Fulham Palace Road,
London W6 9ER
Copyright © 1993 by Nicky Singer
The right of Nicky Singer to be
identified as the author of this work
has been asserted by her in accordance
with the Copyrights, Designs and Patents Act 1988
ISBN 0 09 472 820 8
Set in 10.75pt Ehrhardt
and printed in Great Britain by
Redwood Books, Trowbridge, Wiltshire

A CIP catalogue record for this book
is available from the British Library

For T. J. S. K-S
Aslan

1

The last time I was in this hospital was for the birth of my son. I had not expected a boy.

'Do you want him?' asked a voice above the green gowns and the scissors and the gas and air.

'Not particularly.' I can't have voiced the thought because they laid him on me anyway. I expect God had a good laugh at that. If not then – later.

I am not in a delivery room now. I am in a blue room with two doors and no windows. Some of the outside world filters in through a skylight. Otherwise there are two chairs and a bed with steps and a roll of blue paper to keep it clean. There are some disposable vinyl 'examgloves'; there are chrome instruments in what looks like an egg-box; there is Hibitane obstetric cream; some spatulas and swabs. There are also two boxes of tissues. I'm glad about the tissues.

The nurse – Appleyard, according to the badge pinned at her motherly bosom – comes through the first door, smiles, asks me to 'pop off my things', and then disappears through the unmarked door opposite. Yesterday I popped off my things as requested. Not today. Today I'm sitting on the bed in my flimsy summer dress with my knickers firmly on. I watch my sandalled feet swing a little. I observe the white vinyl floor with the flecks of grey. I don't look at the walls, at the newly stencilled dolphins balancing red balls on their noses. And I don't look at the happy, smiling face of a baby cut from a magazine.

Nurse Appleyard comes back into the room and looks at me sitting like a summer gnome on the bed.

'Well?' she says.

'We didn't do it,' I say. 'Last night we couldn't do it.'

'Why did you come then?' she asks.

It's a question I have asked myself repeatedly since I arose at 7 a.m. in order to be at the hospital at 8.30 a.m. so that Nurse Appleyard might stick a transparent straw high enough inside my vagina to suck out cervical mucus.

'I don't know,' I say. Though I think the answer is comfort.

'What am I going to do with you?' she says.

'Listen?' is what I don't say. I'm not about to tell her how Paul and I fucked last night. I can't call it 'making love'. How we went to bed early, timed ourselves (observing the clinical necessity for eight to ten hours prior to testing) and kissed each other. How we spoke and cajoled and touched and excited. Or tried to. How Paul – this man I have loved for seventeen years – entered me and began to thrust. How we struggled and moaned together, still kissing, and then how he said, still inside me, 'We could do this for another hour, Kate, but I'm not going to come.' And then how he rolled away. When we were students Paul and I sometimes made love three times a day. We've cut down on frequency, but never on urgency. Paul is a smiling and inventive lover. And yet yesterday he rolled away and said (through my shouts), 'I am not a dog. I cannot do it to order.' First failure in seventeen years.

'He couldn't come,' I tell Nurse Appleyard and I burst into tears. She hands me the tissues. The larger, fuller box. Then she puts her arms round me and gives me a big, simple hug.

'They come here for abortions,' she says. 'They come in droves. And then there are people like you.' Her arms tighten. 'I don't say a thing.'

Her hug is making my tears fall harder. I've always been like this. The nicer people are to me, the more I bawl. I pull myself away, wipe my eyes and say, to regain control, 'Do you have children?'

'No.' She lets me go. 'I don't even have a husband. I'd have liked them though.'

She says this utterly without rancour. And I look at her, this lovely, loving middle-aged woman who's just hugged me as my own mother's never hugged me, and I think I should shoot myself. I deserve to be shot, me with my beautiful, passionate husband and my magical three-year-old child. Sam was born in the night. The labour was twenty-four hours. The following night, when he wouldn't settle, the nurses whisked him away to the nursery, 'just so as you can get some kip. We'll bring him back just as soon as he quietens.' They drugged me and I slept without dreams. When I woke at 6 a.m., Sam was not beside me. As I looked at the space where his cot should have been a pang keened through me, a pang such as you couldn't feel unless you'd lost someone you had loved all of your life. In the moment of this grief, they wheeled Sam – crying – into the ward.

6

'He's been fine,' said the nurse. 'Just woken.'

So I woke in response to his cry, I thought. Though I was a hundred yards too far to hear that cry.

Later that morning, as I watched him sleeping in his perspex box, somebody said, 'I love you.' I turned. But the voice was mine, my head talking. I loved this tiny being, so completely dependent and yet so thoroughly, separately himself. They call this bonding. It's very ordinary, but I never imagined it happening to me. Nothing, it seems to me now, prepared me to cross the bridge to motherhood. Did nobody tell me, or did I fail to listen? Or is it actually just impossible to communicate something to somebody unless they know it already?

'My son', I tell Nurse Appleyard, 'was conceived the first month we tried. My husband had to go away on business. We only made love the once.' I laugh. Your chance of conceiving if you make love once a month is 3 per cent, or once every three and a half years. I know a lot about statistics now.

Nurse Appleyard does not laugh. She shrugs. 'You'll be back,' she says. 'Just relax. Next time you come it will be for a pregnancy check. You'll see.' She pats me, a little mournfully.

I blow my nose and leave by Door 1. The corridors are now filling with watermelon-bellied women. One woman has a child in tow, a girl of about twenty months. Classic two-year gap, I think, as I walk into daylight beneath a sign which reads, 'Welcome to the Ante-Natal Clinic'.

I drive to the station, park, and make the 9.46 Victoria train. As usual I choose one of the enclosed, second-class compartments in the first-class carriages. In winter these are cosier and always more silent and when summer comes I find it hard to break the habit. From my briefcase I take Izzy's letter – which I've read already – and the *Independent*. As I wait for the train to leave, I turn to the Gazette and Court Circular.

Millie, Madeleine, Ben, Atalanta, Thomas, Thomas and Rory. These are the children born to *Independent* readers today.

Sometimes I play games with this page. If I open the paper and the first child listed is a boy, I shall have another boy. If a girl, a girl. If there is no child (no paid-for, bold-typed child) then I will never conceive again. It's quite a good gamble. Only about once a month is no child listed. Once a month. Russian roulette. So far my hit rate is about eight girls to one boy. The statistical imbalance of this ratio pleases me.

Two late-thirties men get into the carriage, joining me, a cardi-ganned lady and a sportsbagged youth.

'You're not keen to see the Monet then?' The blond man is speaking. His face is oval, large, relaxed and attractive. He settles himself.

'Well, I don't really like Monet,' replies his dark, tighter companion.

'You've never seen one, have you?'

'Well, now you mention it ...'

'Go on ...' Oval Face nudges his friend.

'He did the big lily pond, didn't he? And the four things of the same thing in different lights?'

Oval Man is silenced.

'It'll take much longer if we go,' wheedles Dark Man gently.

'When I worked in London,' opens Oval anew, 'I ...'

'But that was when they had trams!' ripostes Dark Man.

Typical male banter, point-scoring – but I'm impressed by the lack of self-consciousness. The men do not take account of me or of Cardigan or of Sportsbag. If they were to look, to take account, how would they describe me? Briefcase Woman? No, I have a briefcase but I am not a briefcase woman. My dress is too casual. My sandals Greek. I've had a pair of Greek sandals every summer since Paul and I first Inter-railed across Europe. I suppose I'm really too old to flat-foot along in them now. Thirty-five. Only five more years of childbearing left. Only a hundred and ten shopping days till Christmas. Already my chance of having a Down's baby has increased from 1 in 2000 (age twenty) to 1 in 365. Obsessed Woman? Madwoman? Who do the men see, or not see, sitting opposite them in the train to London?

I unfold Izzy's letter. Eight pages. Sixteen sides of blue-biroed emotion, articulate, open, loving, mature. Too mature. Twenty and just finished finals. She makes me feel old. But then I've always been old to Izzy. I remember when she was born. My father drove me to the hospital. I was fourteen years old. There were no perspex boxes in those days. Izzy was in my mother's arms, wrapped in a piece of white hospital flannelette. My mother looked weary as she held out this unexpected sister for me to view. I remember how tiny Izzy looked and how, instead of a nose, she had two holes in the middle of her face like a pig's snout.

'Got squashed in delivery,' said my mother. 'It will pop out tomorrow.'

It seemed unlikely to me. I thought my sister was deformed. But I smiled because my father was smiling and because it didn't look as if

8

my mother could take much more. She hadn't wanted a second child. Now, I rather doubt that she wanted me either. Her life was so full. If you ask her, she'd say it was the business. Catering. Though in those days it was the delicatessen, running the shop and the sandwich trade. Actually her life was – and still is – full of my father. Those two are like the eternal circle. There is no room for anyone else in their embrace. I looked at Izzy and I felt sorry for her. I didn't love her till much later.

This morning's letter took me by surprise, even though I guessed what it was going to say before I opened it. Izzy and I have always corresponded. She was nine when I left home. I sent her jolly, anecdotal glimpses into my life and she sent me lunatic, misspelt accounts of home. In this we were conspiratorial. We've always laughed a lot. From that first day I dressed Izzy in the little white vest with the tiny pink and white rose stitched at the throat. Izzy must have been about eighteeen months old. Mother came into the bathroom to find us both in tears.

'What's so funny?' she said.

Izzy pointed at the rose, grinned and spluttered. It set me off again. We roared and roared.

'Don't forget to powder her bottom,' my mother said, baffled.

Only once has there been a break in my correspondence with Izzy. This last year and a half. I've had the odd postcard. The odd phone call.

'She's grown up,' said Paul, lover, husband. 'She doesn't need you any more. What did you expect?'

I expected that Izzy had a man. I knew it before she wrote to say so. Yes, that too. Obviously she was telling him and her pillow those things she used to wing to me. What did I expect? It will be like this when Sam grows up, I thought.

'It will be worse,' said my friend Pippa. 'You know,' she continued, 'I think every generation of parents wants something impossible from their children. With us I think it's going to be intimacy. We are not going to be able to bear not knowing what's going on in our children's hearts and minds.'

Thank you, Pippa.

So here I am again with another sixteen-sided letter. It took Izzy sixteen sides to tell me she was in love. Sixteen to explain that the relationship is finished. Izzy is obsessed by balance and connected-ness. Later I shall mention the sixteen sides and she'll find it relevant. Today's letter is very brave. She is disbelieving, frightened, lonely but also exhilarated and freed. She feels very small in a very big world.

9

She describes the split with such honesty and appears to have behaved so sensibly and with such genuine kindliness that I feel a little redundant. Why do I always want to be the emotional white knight?

'The things that happened in my twenties, they set up expectations too. It's not just the expectations of childhood, you know.' This is what the Oval Man is saying now. I've been half-listening to their conversation all the time. As their tone changes, I turn up the volume. These two men in a carriage of strangers are talking as I've never heard men talk before. Straight men anyway. They are talking about things which matter.

'No, I don't want to go abroad,' continues Oval. 'I think that's just a different place to set up the same sort of relationships. That's how I see it.'

'Commitments, material, psychological – they nudge you. You don't choose life's pattern. It chooses you.'

'Yeah. That's it,' says Oval. 'It's like a man stuck in a traffic jam. There are some things you just have to accept.'

'Excuse me,' I want to say, 'you have to plan. To prepare. To engage. Do you think I'm just going to lie down and accept the absence of Millie, Madeleine, Ben, Atalanta, Thomas, Thomas and Rory?' I don't say this, of course, but I do allow myself to look directly at Oval. What strikes me is that he looks happy. Paul sometimes looks like this. Content. Easy with himself. His life. It outrages me. I rarely see this look on women's faces. Why is that?

As we draw towards Victoria, the conversation reverts to Monet.

'Let's toss for it,' says Oval. 'Heads Monet, tails Michael.'

Dark Man gets out a ten pence piece.

'OK.' He tosses. 'Oh no! Let's do it again. Best of three!'

'Come on . . .' says Oval.

Dark Man tosses again. 'Oh for God's sake! Best of five!'

He throws a third time. It is obviously heads again.

'Pretty conclusive, I'd say!'

Oval Man wins. In my experience Oval Man always wins. But then, looking at Dark Man, I think they will not go to the Monet after all. Or they will go and the queue will be so long they'll decide not to wait. However, Oval Man will still win because, whatever happens, he won't mind.

Me – I mind about everything.

2

I walk from Piccadilly into Soho. My office is at the triangular junction of Old Compton Street and Moor Street, in what, in the States, they'd call a Flat Iron building. Of course, in Soho you don't notice that, only that it's located above Ed's Diner. Pippa and I have the top floor. There are four flights of tiny stairs, a kitchenette and loo on a half-landing and then the office itself. It's a triangular room with windows each side. I sit at the apex and Pippa sits on the base line. It's a very feminine room. The floor is boarded and scattered with dilapidated Turkish rugs. There are plants and plant pots and real coffee and too many books with too few shelves. We keep meaning to do shelves. The files are hand-me-downs and both of our desks are cluttered. Mine more so than Pippa's. We don't have assistants or secretaries. We do have computers. On the door Pippa has pinned a hand-flourished notice: 'ArtsAid: Pippa Gates and Kate Francis: Walk right in.'

I walk right in.

'Hi! How are you? How was it?' Pippa waves, salutes, telephone in hand.

'OK. Tolerable. Tell you later.' Yesterday I gave Pippa a scrape-by-scrape account of Monday's post-coital. And she was there when, in the afternoon, I phoned for the results.

'Well?'

'One out of ten,' I told her. Up to now I've always been good at exams.

'What does it mean?' she asked.

'Mainly dead sperm. Mainly not moving. I have to test again. Tomorrow. In case it was just too early in the cycle.'

Pippa nods, just as she did yesterday, speaks into the receiver. She has a wide, pinkish smile and blonde hair which she pins inexpertly on the top of her head. She's thirty-nine, but looks much younger as she

11

has one of those compact bodies which allows her to look good in young, fashionable clothes.

'Tell him I'll call back.' She replaces the receiver. 'Glenda Jackson's confirmed. Ditto Russell-Beale and the Adelphi's come in.'

'Terrific,' I say. I hope these are phone messages. It's very childish but, despite the fact that we are co-directors, I can't stand Pippa reading my post. I like to slide my own fingers under my own envelope flaps and be first with the secrets inside. I'm like this even about bills.

I sit down at my desk and check my wall calendar for meetings and my Silvine notebook for tasks. ArtsAid is a small charity Pippa and I founded in the excitement of Band Aid and Comic Relief. This year we are mounting our most ambitious project to date – ArtsAid Day. On Sunday 10 November, London will be transformed into one huge venue for the arts – with all artists performing for free and all proceeds going to charity. Pippa is in charge of classical music, dance, street theatre and the big art auction and I am responsible for pop music, theatre and the movies.

Today I'm working on Sonnets and Soliloquies. From 10 in the morning the ICA theatre will reverberate with Fausts and Hamlets and Macbeths and Dark Ladies. I have a provisional list of the great and good who may take part. I have teased personal contacts, laid flattery traps, written letters, extracted verbal promises, sweet-talked agents, bypassed agents, called in favours, checked dates and schedules. And now, with my list of numbers beside me, I'm moving in for the kill. By the end of the day I want to be able to count the daggers before my eyes, see where Christ's blood streams in the firmament and live your epitaph to make. Then I will begin the schedule, space the unsexed Lady Macbeths, control the flow of the famous and the less famous, chalk in my stand-bys, draft a blurb, a programme and then, and only then, pass the project on. I will be charming and ruthless. It is all so easy, so enjoyable, so autopilot, even when things go wrong – for I have reasonable expectations, margins for error, contingency plans. It is not like taking a three-year-old to the supermarket. That's hard work. That's a journey into the unknown where the dividing line between success and failure isn't marked on the map. To the left the marsh of humiliation, to the right the quicksand of your sanity. Look out! Beware the bridge to the frozen whiting! Yes, they've rearranged the freezer cabinets yet again. And it's going to take just that little bit too long to find the fish, and Sam's mithering will become moaning and the moaning wheedling and the noise will be like a needle in my ear and somebody will suddenly shriek and it'll be me at the check-out, in front of a lot of childless persons tching and tutting and staring and then screaming from nowhere: *Take her away! Unfit! Unfit!*

Yet who is it who feels a sense of achievement when she returns from this quiet and easy office, this three-day-a-week job? It's me! Me who feels that I've earned that gin and tonic and that hour in front of the television. And me again who, after a day with Sam, irons and tidies and gets out that picture hook just so that I have done something, so Paul sees that I have done something, to justify my existence in the world, and his – mainly – having to pay for it.

'And you want another kid!' says Pippa.

I do. This job which is so meaningful, so socially useful, so impressive as a topic of dinner-table conversation (not that Paul and I go to many dinner parties now), this job no longer holds my attention. Before, when I used to walk along Old Compton Street in the early evening, I'd smell the heat of coffee and of tarmac and of deals being struck in bars, I'd watch the gas flaming round restaurants and see the burn in the eyes of Soho's acquisitors, I'd feel the throb of whores, of expectation, of the city. I'd feel alive. Now I see dirt in the gutters and a host of self-important briefcases clutching on to fat hands and hollow hearts; a mass of moving head-down humanity, and me moving with them. And I think, why? What's the point? It's all suddenly flim-flam. None of it compares with the jerking cry of a new-born. None of it touches me the way my son's fingertips touch me as he closes his tiny arms about my neck and says, 'I love you, Mummy.'

'So you really want to be a vegetable again,' says Pippa.

Why not? I'm good at being a vegetable. I loved those days when just to arrive at an evening was an accomplishment and when living was feeding and shitting in rhythmical cycles.

'Rot,' says Pippa. 'You hated being pregnant and you couldn't wait to get back to work.'

That's true too. Memory is a selective thing. My inability to conceive a second child makes me forget. The older I get the less things seem to be true anyway, true for all time that is. Pippa is more certain.

'I'm thirty-nine,' she says.

Pippa has things arranged, organized. Pippa makes me (Paul would laugh) look like a planning dilettante. Like me she works part time for ArtsAid, but on her Thursdays and Fridays she does highly paid (she's been to business school) consultancy work. Her son, Josh, is just over one year old and his prime carer is his father, though Gran helps out on Mondays and Tuesdays if Richard wants to go to the

London Library. Richard was made redundant when the *Correspondent* folded and although he was head-hunted by the *Independent*, he declined a job. Embracing his freedom, began working from home, planning his book on The New Europe. It's a very modern marriage and Pippa looks glowing on it. My more traditional partnership with Paul, him as the main bread-winner and my earnings not covering much more than the nanny, seems feeble beside it. I blame Paul. His job as a commissioning editor for Classics and Ancient History is not very flexible. Actually, it's me. I couldn't bear not to be with Sam at least half the week.

'Don't you feel you're missing out?' I ask Pippa.

'Dear God,' she says, 'Josh is much better off with Richard. He's infinitely more patient than me.'

Pippa went back to work when Josh was eight weeks old. It took me eight months. Maybe I am a vegetable. But I don't want to be like my mother. She worked all through my childhood. And Izzy's too. I don't know what we missed out on but I feel a lack – I feel that, if it wasn't for Izzy, I'd be a little unloved.

I'm nearly at the end of my morning list of phone calls. Lucrative film deals permitting, I've tied down three actresses, four actors and a comedian. The comedian was unexpected and therefore a bonus. Two television stars, tipped off by friends, have phoned in to offer their services. And, quite by chance, I've discovered Woody Allen's going to be in town that weekend. I've pencilled him in for the South Bank. It will be about 70/30 if I can get to speak with him personally. A good morning's work.

'How you doing?' I ask Pippa.

'Good enough for lunch at the Trat,' she says.

We go to the cheap Italian place opposite. We wave rather than order because I always have Spaghetti Vongole and Pippa always has Lasagne. Most times Pippa also has wine. I don't know how she keeps her figure.

'OK, shoot,' she says.

Pippa has been following my infertility with a studied, almost caring interest. Infertility. That voodoo word I wouldn't say about myself for over a year, though they wrote it on my card that first ever appointment. I'd visited the doctor after a thirteen-day period. By that time I'd been trying to conceive for six months. My GP referred me to a specialist: Mr James Baboneau. Baboneau sent me for a blood test. The first of many. In the box labelled 'Reason for Investigation' he wrote (in his elaborate black hand) 'Subfertility'. So there it was. A woman with a child, who had spent a mere six months trying to

conceive (the average at my advanced time of life is nine months),
went to her ordinary doctor as an ordinary patient and came away a
card-carrying member of The Subfertile. And labels matter. I always
think.

'Come on, come on!'

Pippa's impatient but not very sympathetic. This makes her an
ideal person for me to relay information to.

'We didn't do it,' I tell her. 'We didn't fuck.'

'What!'

'Being obliged. It turned Paul off. He couldn't perform.'

'You're kidding!' she says. 'Do you think being forced would stop
Richard?'

This particular joke – that if you can't conceive, it doesn't really
matter because at least you can have fun trying – has worn very thin on
me. Anyone but Pippa would probably have had my fist in their
mouth. I smile, eat clams and say, 'Why did you wait so long to have
kids?' I know the answer to this perfectly well. But I want to press her
about her age. I've suddenly come over mean.

'Busy, busy, busy,' says Pippa. 'And Richard wasn't that
interested. Not when he was a foreign correspondent, jetting all over
the place.'

'And it doesn't bother you,' I say, 'being thirty-nine?'

'Not much I can do about it.'

Her airiness defeats me immediately.

'Paul always wanted to have kids. Been asking me for ages. Nice
irony, isn't it?' One of the things I love about Paul is that he never
mentions this fact. Never says, if only we'd started earlier. Sometimes
I think 'if only' is not in his vocabulary.

'Women in the *News of the World* have babies at forty-four every
day of the week. At thirty-five you're almost a baby yourself!'

'But I want to have three children,' I say. 'At least.' I'm astonished
at this remark and not sure whether it is true.

'You're some sucker,' says Pippa.

'Perhaps I just want', I say, 'the choice.'

'Sorry,' says Pippa. And she means it.

'Actually I think that's one of the things I find most difficult of all.
Accepting – no, not accepting because I haven't and I won't – but
facing the fact that I haven't the choice. Or don't seem to have. That
this is something utterly arbitary. Out of my control. That no matter
what I do, or how I plan or what I'm prepared to sacrifice, I can't have
it. Just can't.'

'Not just yet anyway,' interrupts Pippa. I'm grateful for that.

'And it's so unreasonable. So inexplicable. To be apparently perfectly fertile, even above averagely so, and then, for no reason, to have this happen. It makes me feel out of control of everything. All parts of my life, not just this one. Like being burgled.'

'But there is a reason surely,' says Pippa. 'Your low hormone levels.'

Brilliant memory, this Pippa.

'*Was* a reason,' I say. 'The Clomid's supposed to have restored the levels. According to the tests I'm now ovulating perfectly normally. Have been for months. Seven months.'

'Interesting what you say about it being "unreasonable" though,' Pippa continues, thinking. 'Who said life had to be reasonable? That's the twentieth century for you. The rise and rise of rationalism. We're born and bred to expect things to add up, to be subject to scientific scrutiny, scientific proof. If it doesn't fit, sling it out. We can't cope.'

I enjoy this about Pippa, the 'masculine' (as Paul would say) cast of her mind. She can't just gossip. She has to pull some intellectual theory out of the conversation.

'Eat your pasta,' I say. 'It's getting cold.'

'What?' she says.

But she eats anyway.

We return to the office and to the afternoon. I have to leave more messages than in the morning because more people are out. This irritates me. But where I make contact I score a ninety-five per cent success rate. At six o'clock I think about a gin and tonic and ring home.

There is a pause and then Tessa says, 'Hello.' I can never work out whether it's the pause or the way she says hello that makes her sound stupid.

'Hi,' I say. 'It's me. How was your day?'

'We went down the front,' she says.

I wait for more information.

'He liked it.'

I remind myself, not for the first time, that I didn't employ Tessa for her story-telling capabilities.

'He threw stones. Sam,' she calls, 'it's Mummy, come and talk!'

What sort of stones? Large or small? Pebbles or rocks? What colour? How many? And did he go nearer the sea than usual? Or keep his customary, wary distance? Did he laugh? Did his eyes shine? Did he deliberately choose a heavy embedded rock, lift and puff, stagger towards the shore, attempt an over-arm throw and then watch in astonishment as the rock thudded at his feet? And what did they do when they weren't at the front? Where did they go? Who did they see?

'Hello?' says Sam's voice, sounding intrigued and grown-up.

'Hello, darling,' I say. 'What did you do today?'

'I had fish-fingers. I had peas. I had potato. Bye!'

I hear him scurry away.

'Hello?' Paul comes on the line.

'Hi,' I say, 'you're home early.'

'Yuh.'

'Good day?'

'So so.'

I wait for him to ask about the hospital.

'When will you be back?' he asks.

3

I arrive home at 8.30 and let myself into our cool, quiet house. Along the corridor and down three steps is the kitchen. The kitchen light is on, as are the patio lamps which illumine our small square of garden beyond. But this is merely forgetfulness. Paul will be in the drawing-room. The door is ajar and I go in. Sometimes I wish he would rise to greet me, but he never does. He's sitting in the back half of the room, in the green corner chair with the gold tassles which have come unglued. He's reading by the light of a small lamp set on the table beside him. At first I think he's working but then I see the book is bound and, even upside-down, I know it's Larkin.

Paul was reading poetry the first time I ever laid eyes on him. It was a March day with an unexpectedly blue sky and a pale lilting sun. The sort of day which makes you feel, rather than know, that the winter will finally end. Paul was sitting beneath the copper beech in the quad, coat off but jumpers thickly on. Nobody else had stopped for this tiny moment of spring. Students walked briskly round paths and between staircases. Impulsively I crossed the grass to join him, threw down my own coat and got out my own book. He didn't lift his head then either. The texts spewing from his bag were mainly plays: *The Eumenides, Agamemnon, Electra, Philoctetes, Medea*. But the book on his knee was Walt Whitman. I recognized the edition, the page, the 'Song of Myself'.

> I celebrate myself, and sing myself,
> And what I assume you shall assume,
> For every atom belonging to me as good belongs to you.

I remember that beginning so well, the smoke of my own breath and the curve of Paul's mouth. I couldn't have told you then that his hair was brown or his eyes grey. All I saw was his mouth. Paul had – and has – the most beautiful lips, where to look is to want to kiss. His mouth smiles a little even in repose and his teeth are bitingly white and even.

' "The atmosphere is not a perfume," ' I quoted him, ' "it has no taste of distillation, it is odorless." '

He turned towards me and took off his glasses. I hadn't noticed the glasses before.

' "It is for my mouth forever, I am in love with it,
I will go to the bank by the wood and become undisguised and naked,
I am mad for it to be in contact with me." '

As I finished, he laughed a little, nodded, put his glasses back on and then returned to his own absorption. His self-containment captivated me. I picked up my coat, made a show of leaving, passed too close to him and thought I felt his hand. I didn't. It was weeks before he touched me.

'Hello.' It's me speaking.

Paul puts a finger on the Larkin text and looks up.

'Hi.'

'Have you eaten?'

'I thought you'd have something on the train.'

I nod, go into the kitchen and fix myself a sandwich. Grated Edam cheese with horseradish sauce and sliced red pepper. Sometimes I eat on the train. Sometimes I don't. After a while Paul joins me, stands in the kitchen door.

'Everything OK today?' he asks.

'Which everything?'

'Work? Pippa?'

'I went to the hospital,' I inform him.

'Mm?'

'You forgot, didn't you?'

'What?'

'Forgot. Failed to remember. Didn't think about it. Didn't give it the time of day.'

'No, I didn't forget.'

'Oh, I see. Just wasn't important enough to mention, is that it?'

'I just didn't think you'd really go. I didn't think there was much point.'

'Oh – no point at all!'

'Kate . . .' He crosses to where I'm sitting, reaches out his hand.

'You've got to go for a sperm test,' I tell him. I've known about the sperm test for two weeks but have been waiting for an appropriate moment to tell him. This is not the moment.

'I already went for one!' Paul objects.

'Please don't let's have all that trauma again! For Christ's sake, Paul!'

'What are you getting so worked up about!'

'You! Your precious prick! I go for blood tests and internals and smears and scrapes and have doctors shoving their fat hands up me every day of the week and one mention of a quick wank for you and you're in spasm!'

'Who's in spasm!'

Pippa's opinion on this – for what it's worth – is that genitals prove God is a man. Who but a man would design women's genitals, which are so subject to scrutiny, on the inside and men's, which are so fucking untouchable, on the outside?

'But I already tested!' Paul complains again.

'So what? I test for ovulation every three minutes. Fertility changes. You might have gone downhill since last time.'

Paul returns to the drawing-room.

'I'm putting the papers on the dresser,' I shout after him. 'You've got to do it this week. I've got an appointment with Baboneau on 16 August.'

There is no response.

'Do you know who Baboneau is?' I shout. Then I eat the rest of my sandwich.

After a while I go into the drawing-room and apologize.

'I'm sorry,' I say, 'but it would be nice if you took an interest.' I was never very good at the straight apology.

Paul just shrugs and shakes his head.

Sometimes his refusal to engage maddens me. Not tonight. To-night I go up and see Sam.

Sam's room is square and dusky pink. His curtains, which are too thin for summer, float with pink and purple birds of paradise. His bookcases and cupboards and drawers are spatter-painted in blues and ochres and overdrawn with suns and moons and rainbows. I painted them myself in the madness of pre-birth. The colours hum gently in the light that spills from Meadow Sweet Cottage. This tiny china house with its china dresser and china fireplace and family of china rabbits was a gift from Izzy. The night-light was hers when she was a child and I was very touched that she should think to give it to Sam. He's afraid of the dark and the cottage has shone for him in all the nights he can remember. There is dust on the rabbits' floor and a dead daddy-long-legs next to Pa Rabbit's chair. I keep meaning to clean it.

As usual Sam is sprawled on, rather than in, his bed. He's three and a half now, long and leggy. Sometimes he lies horizontally across his pillow. Tonight he's lying at a 45-degree angle, his pyjamas parted in the middle. I see the taut flesh of his stomach and the hollow of his belly-button. I love this hollow and the thought that it was here that Sam and I once joined. I think the belly-button is much underrated. I see it as evidence of an unbroken cord which stretches back, child to mother, mother to grandmother, generation to generation, until the beginning of time. Does the fact that Sam is a boy break the chain? Or will he just daisy-chain with his wife so that the link will continue, forward with him and his children until the end of time? As Izzy says, we are all connected.

Gently, I lift my son and lay him straighter in his bed. He moans a little, this sleeping cub. I tuck the duvet around him and stroke his soft cheek. Asleep he looks like his father, only blonder and more innocent. But then Paul always looks particularly beautiful asleep. Is that so for everyone? Does even an ugly man slip into a generous repose? Does sleep smooth aggression from the thug? I trace a finger down Sam's neck. I ache at his loveliness.

Downstairs, thinking of belly-buttons, I ring my mother.

'Hello, Jean,' I say. Sometimes I think, if she had allowed us to call her Mummy, then we would have been closer.

'Hello, Kate.'

There is a pause.

'How are you?' It's me asking the question.

'Rushed off my feet, of course. Big do this weekend. Christening. Cake for a hundred and twenty. Canapés. Spinach roulade. Smoked salmon and horseradish whirls. Italian rice balls. Miniature prawn galettes. Stuffed canary tomatoes. Dips. Asparagus spears. Fairly up-market. You know the sort of thing, Kate.'

I do. I even know the prices, though they change more often. I remember the weekend I went to visit my parents after finishing my politicians series. I'd interviewed six members of the Cabinet in as many days. The Foreign Secretary had invited me to his home. I knew what books were in his library, what colour loo-paper he had in his downstairs toilet, what cartoons were pinned to his study walls, with what grace his wife made coffee for us, how he commented, school-master-fashion, on my use of the word 'hubris', what his views were on religion, on sexuality (his son was a self-confessed gay), on leadership and on the qualities which maketh man. I thought my mother would be interested. I was bursting with the story.

She listened, or appeared to be listening, if not agog then at least politely. She nodded, even said 'Mm!' and then suddenly her eyes lit with excitement.

'Curried chicken timbales!' she shouted. 'That's it, Derek! They would be perfect!'

And my father, finger paused in a recipe book, said, 'Jean, you're a genius!'

I tried not to mind. I reminded myself that the stuff of my life and the stuffing of hers were one and the same. Neither was more important. That curried chicken timbales were real in a way that perhaps my glimpse into power was not real. That, finally, life is measured out with coffee-spoons and who am I to sneer? But the discovery that other people have the right to exist, that, in their own individual way, their lives are as intensely lived as mine and thus carry the same weight as mine, that was a difficult lesson for me. As difficult as the first time I realized, aged twenty-one, that people could be more stupid than me yet more happy.

'How's Derek?' I ask.

'Gone Greek,' says my mother. 'Baklava. Bougatsa, Skaltsounia, Floyeres, Melopitta. You name it. Pedi Tis Pittas. Whole house stinks of honey.'

'Send me a Red Cross parcel,' I say.

There's a pause. My need for her to ask about me is palpable.

'How's Paul?' she asks.

'Fine.' My mother likes Paul. He smiles, admires her creations, and only tastes if invited. She once said she thought he was 'too good' for me. She's appalled by the Marks and Sparks dinners I serve him. Or rather, with which we serve ourselves. Only mother wouldn't get the distinction. Paul likes Jean, toys with her. 'The way to a man's heart,' she tells him (telling me), 'is through his stomach.' Paul's wistfulness would break your heart. 'Oh I know, Jean,' he shrugs. 'But what can one do?'

'And Sam?' my mother asks. 'How's he?'

'Beautiful,' I say. 'As always.' She's not the fondest grandparent. Her grandson's praises are mainly sung by me.

'So pleased,' she says. 'Can't really stop, Kate. Icing, you know.'

I know.

'Bye.'

'Bye, Kate. Derek sends love.'

I doubt that.

'See you,' I euphemize and put the phone down, hearing the snap of umbilical and electrical cords.

Paul comes into the hall.

'Who was that?' he asks.

'My effusive mother.'

'And how is the Summer Pudding?'

He's not being rude. At this time of year my mother normally makes two dozen Summer Puddings, 'because they freeze so well'.

'Overtaken by cake and baklava.'

'Oh Brave New World,' remarks Paul, heading for a second coffee. I decide to ring Izzy.

She moved flats last term and I haven't yet visited her new place. It unnerves me not being able to picture where she is. I think of the phone ringing in a huge empty room.

'Hello?' It's Jeff, one of her flatmates.

'Hi, it's Kate. Is Izzy there?'

'Hang about.'

He puts down the phone and shouts, 'Izz? Izz?'

I do not believe her flat can be so large he doesn't know whether she's there or not. How can you not know who's living and breathing not ten yards from you?

'She's out,' decides Jeff.

'Do you know when she might be back?'

'No idea. Don't know where she's gone.'

I know where she's gone.

'Thanks,' I say. 'Bye.'

Izzy's gone to visit God.

4

At 8.15 on Wednesday morning Rosemary rings in to tell me my nanny's ill. Rosemary is the older woman with whom Tessa shares a flat. She's polite and apologetic.

'She was sick *all* night,' says Rosemary. 'And she's running a terrible temperature.'

I've noticed how Tessa almost always runs temperatures on a Wednesday. Wednesday is the day I sometimes work from home. I find it easier to draft reports or press releases or to write programmes in the telephone silence of my own house. Not having to commute also gives me a longer day. Tessa, on the other hand, obviously believes that if I'm at home, I can't be doing any serious work so I might as well be looking after my son. The fact that I pay her to do this job doesn't, as far as I can judge, enter into her calculations.

'Tell her to get better soon,' I tell Rosemary. Sometimes Tessa is genuinely sick. I've seen her. Paul says it's alcohol poisoning from the pub where she works in the evenings.

I go upstairs, still in my dressing-gown. Paul has just finished shaving.

'That was Tessa,' I tell him. 'She's vomiting.'

'Not again!' Paul splashes himself with something from a black Geo Trumper bottle.

'Can you take the day off?' I ask him.

'Don't be ridiculous.'

'Why is it ridiculous! Looks like I'm going to have to take the day off!' I find this assumption, that Tessa is employed so that I can work, rather than that we may both work, profoundly irritating.

'I've got a lot to do today,' I say.

'So have I! I've got meetings!'

Meetings are good. Clearly I don't have meetings today.

'You get five days a week to work,' I tell him. 'I only get the three.

You lose a day and it's only a fifth of your time. For me, it's a third. Ergo, the loss of my time is more crucial.'

'Can't you ring Julia?' Paul suggests, putting on his shirt, doing up the buttons, preparing for his suit and his office.

'Why can't you ring Julia!' That's another thing – why is child care always my problem, my responsibility to fix, unfix, refix?

'For God's sake, Kate, I hardly know the woman!'

I go downstairs and ring Julia. We gave birth on the same day, had beds next to each other in hospital. Her son William is Sam's best friend. Now she has another son, Daniel. Daniel is eleven months old, precisely the age my second child would be. If I had one.

'Julia, it's me. Look, I hate to do this to you again, and believe me I owe you, like hell do I owe you, but...'

'She's not sick again!'

'Is it Wednesday?'

'Kate, I'd love to have Sam, but we're going to Chichester. It's my Mum's birthday. We're staying the night.'

'Oh, fine. Look, I'm really sorry to ask...'

'No, no, not at all, I...'

'I've got to buy you dinner. Have some adult talk.'

'Yes, let's do that.'

I put the phone down on thirty quid. Sam wanders out of the playroom where he has been watching a Teenage Mutant Hero Turtle video.

'I thought you were getting dressed,' he remarks.

'I was,' I say. 'I was going to work too. As it is, you get to be so lucky and have me all day.'

'No Tessa?' he inquires, his face brightening.

'No Tessa. Tessa's sick.'

'I don't like Tessa,' he says and returns to the embrace of the mutants.

I'm a little ambivalent about Tessa myself. I like her because she's forthright and direct, because she's strong and physically competent and has kept my son safe for over two and a half years. I like her because she loves Sam. And the depth of her love surprises me, given how much she has lacked for love herself.

'I should take what she tells you with a pinch of salt,' says Paul. 'A large pinch.'

She's a child from a broken home. Her father hit her mother and she spent six months of her childhood in a refuge for battered women. When she was nine she went out for a burger and was raped by the Chinese man who co-owned the burger bar. When she arrived home

25

three hours late (she'd had to walk back from the airfield where he'd dumped her), her mother didn't even ask what had kept her. Of course, I didn't find out all these things at once, but in jigsaw pieces over the years. In the main, I believe her, because of the detail. In her handbag she keeps folded pieces of silver paper, sweet-papers from the toffees her father gave her when she was ten. His first gift to her since the split four years earlier.

I tried to remember these things when Tessa moonlighted on me. She was cleaning for a woman on Tuesday afternoons, and she just took Sam with her and let him amuse himself as she earned extra money. When challenged, at first she denied everything. Vehemently. Later she changed her plea.

'Sam was quite happy,' she said. 'More interesting for him than being at home.'

When Paul and I tried fine moral distinctions on her, she ran out into the street, slamming doors and crying. I caught her at the bus-stop, tried to calm her down. I thought she was going to hit me. I invited her back.

'Why?' said Paul.

'Why?' said Pippa.

'You're trying to be her mother now,' said Izzy.

'No luck with Julia?' Paul comes downstairs in his immaculate suit. He looks tall and elegant. He calls Sam to say goodbye, but doesn't encourage a kiss for fear of Sam's breakfast mouth. He kisses me.

'*Carpe diem*,' he says as he opens the door on the July sunshine. 'Who'd want to be indoors on a day like this anyway?'

An hour and a half later, Sam and I are on the train to Lewes. There has been no trouble about socks today. About putting on pants and trousers and the fact that his Batman T-shirt is in the wash ('I like it dirty, Mum'), no hiding under bedclothes and shrieking into corners, 'But I only want one shoe on today!'

In the train, Sam is king of his carriage. He waves and beams. We are going to Lewes Castle. The journey is fifteen minutes. Each time we pass through a tunnel, Sam's hands fly to his face, holding his own gasp of excitement. What is so enchanting about this tunnel of black? The suddenness of our rush into it? The fact that we burst back into light? Or just that we normally travel by car and this is all new to Sam? Did God feel so delighted as he called each new thing into being at the beginning of time? I remember how Paul and I took Sam away to France when he was about fourteen months old. We stayed on the Ile

26

d'Oleron, five minutes' forest walk from a sand white beach. The first morning we emerged from the trees to see a strip of burning white and the blue, blue ocean beyond. I set Sam down on the sand and for a moment he stood quite still. Then he lifted his arms and shouted – for the first time – 'Sea!' And it was as though he had not just named the sea but invented it. I stood in the shadow of his exuberance and wondered when and how we lose this freshness, this power to create.

Lewes station comes all too quickly. Sam would fight to stay on the train if the promise of the castle didn't pull him to the platform. We exit and cross the road bridge. Sam looks down at the track, and marvels at a digger half a mile away. I hurry him, I'm not sure why as we have a day without limit. On our way up the hill towards the centre of town we pass a small café.

'I want a drink,' he says.

'Pardon?'

'Please,' he adds with a sigh.

My engagement in the ritual is automatic. Too late I see I've lost. I look at my watch, 10.40. Almost elevenses.

'OK,' I say.

The café has round tables with red and white chequered cloths. The menu is mainly vegetarian and the cakes real and crumbly. Three women sit at different tables drinking solitary cups of coffee. They are middle-aged women, on their way to or from shops or libraries. They have come in, I think, for the shade and the quiet. I notice with relief that there is a garden out the back. The tables are too close here as well, but no one else is in this square of sunlight. And somehow noise in a garden is more acceptable than noise inside. I place our order as quickly as I can and steer Sam out. I choose a corner table which has some shade from a tree. Sam wants to sit more centrally, so he can monitor progress inside the café, and wave at the solitary women. We negotiate.

'Your drink will be coming soon,' I inform him. 'You'll need to be sitting down. Here.'

But the drink does not come. It's a milk shake. There is no one else waiting to be served, and yet it still takes nearly ten minutes to make a banana shake. 'The customer shall bear no liability for any destruction caused by or during any unreasonable delay,' I was tempted to etch that into the walls of the pub where we once waited forty-five minutes for a round of ham sandwiches. Don't managements know about children? But even as I think this, I realize there is a change. Sam has come to sit at my table. He is engaging me in conversation, he wants to know why there are brass fish stuck into the flower beds.

27

'They're decorative,' I tell him, 'garden sculptures.'

'Fish go in the sea,' he remarks. 'Normally.'

He smiles, a bright, clean little boy who has obviously grown up a little since I was last in a café alone with him. How long ago is that? How have I missed this little growing-up?

At last his drink comes, and with it an oat slice with apricots. He eats methodically and hungrily, squeezing the crumbs between his fingers and thumb. I watch him and drink Diet Coke from a glass. He finishes.

'Let's go,' he says and is down at once.

And we go because it's easier that way.

As we climb towards the heart of the town he stops to look over a garden wall. There is a rockery with a waterfall splashing into a pool beneath. Intently, he watches the fall of the water.

'It's like the rain butt, Mum,' he announces.

I take his hand. The workings of his mind are so naked. He defines what he does not know by what he does know. Orders his experience, patterns it. This is only what we all do, or try to do. But, watching him, I'm aware for the first time how slippage may occur. His assumptions about the height, descent and pooling of water are adequate. But if he was talking of love? If he was matching his assumptions against those of another?

We pass along the main street. I'd like to dawdle, looking at the prices of antiques or the cut of the Lewes ladies' frocks. But we may only stop if a shop interests Sam. None of them do. We are soon at the tiny museum from which tickets to the castle may be bought. I pay. If Paul was with us he would buy a guide. By the end of the day he would know, and he would remember, all the historical details of the place. As it is, I shall only remember the anecdotal, I shall go away with just a feeling for the castle and time we spent there.

We cross the road to the wrought-iron entrance. Through the gates, Sam has already seen the cannon. That will be our first twenty-minute stop. We discuss the powder, the shot, the cannonballs. When we get to the lighted taper and 'the olden days', I move Sam on, in need of firmer ground. We progress up the gravelled hill towards the first of the turrets. This hewn tower of stone seems no longer to belong to the main crown of the castle. It stands separate and apart. A bridge takes us across a truncated dry moat. We enter the cool first floor. Sam already has his foot on the first stone stair. He does not know where it will lead, but he is going. Step by step, hand over hand he climbs. At each new floor he stops briefly, runs to the arrow windows, scans the countryside and then is on again, up and up. The stairs get narrower and more worn and I begin to be fearful of his tread. What if he should fall? I need to be below him, to catch him. I need to be above him to ensure the steps are safe, to negotiate him past the descent of any other visitor.

'Wait!' I cry.

Sam does not want to wait. He wants to go up, wherever up is. He's breathless and laughing. He cannot wait.

'It's dangerous,' I shout.

He stops.

'Why is it?'

'Because you could fall and I might not be able to hold you, best creature of my heart.' I do not say this to my son. I do not talk to him of death, though every time I look at him, I think it.

We go on again, more slowly now, and emerge through a small opening on to the sunlit roof of the tower. Sam urges me to lift him, so he may look over the parapet. I lift and cling to him. He struggles to position himself on the battlement. There are two feet of flat wall and then a hundred-foot drop.

'No!' I pull him back.

'But I can't see!'

It is dangerous but I am also over-reacting. As I lifted him, I felt the panic again, the caged bird that beats and screams in my breast. I've always been fearful for Sam. When he was just a few days old I worried that I would fall down the stairs carrying him. But this is not the same. The bird has grown and the cage is smaller.

'You'll make yourself sick,' says Paul.

I am sick already. I see the shadow of death everywhere, in a boiling kettle, in a single peanut, in the back seat of my mother's car. And, in the absence of a second child, the shadow has deepened, lengthening with the lengthening months.

'That's simply irrational,' says Paul.

It simply is. For another child could never lessen the loss of Sam. Yet the shadow is there and lengthening.

'We have to go down now,' I say.

'But I want to see!'

'You want to have time for the other tower, don't you? It's a bigger one!'

And so I promise to take him to another precipice. I do it deliberately. If I do not confront the fear, and go to the edge with him every day, I will construct another cage. And Sam will be in it.

The second tower is bigger and the steps broader. Sam's tread is still light and joyful. But there are more people climbing this tower and we have to be careful, to stop and flatten ourselves against the walls. Sam likes it.

'I'm a ghostie,' he says.

We come out again into sunlight and this time I lift Sam without his asking. We can see for twenty miles. It bores Sam. He wants to go down again. I go through the trap door first and, as I wait for his legs to appear above me, I feel again the flutter in my breast. But he comes.

Back down on the grassy innards of castle we stop and rest. I sit under a huge horse-chestnut tree which must, presumably, have seeded itself there. Sam inspects the floodlights trained on the towers. He puts his hand down to see where the electrics join the earth.

'Don't touch that bit,' I shout.

Sam moves on, presses his face to the glass to look at the light-bulbs.

I could adopt.

No one is allowed to suggest this to me. I alone may contemplate it in the secret hurt of my heart. I would like to adopt. I feel I have the love to give. But I know, and fear to know, that my own unconceived child would still weep within me.

'I'm not sure one should have another child,' says Pippa, 'what with the population explosion. If one cares about the planet, that is. Adopting, on the other hand, is humanitarian and ecologically sound.'

Oh Pippa. You have the choice. It would be a positive decision for you. For me, it would feel like a failure. 'Ridiculous!' Paul would say. Were I ever to tell him.

Of course, they wouldn't let me adopt anyway. If you are fertile, you may be the worst and most loveless of human beings and yet have a child. If you are infertile there are rules and regulations, pieces of paper, other people's expectations, judgements. They would say, 'She is too old.' They would look at my life, at my work and say, 'Besides, she can't even be bothered to stay at home and look after her own son.'

I look at my son. He's building a pile of stones beneath the floodlight. His own little castle. Could I be with him every day? Would it be good for him? For me? Today is different, today is a holiday and we are moving in time with each other. But every day? At the supermarket and the dentist, over the washing-up and the ironing? Is that what it is to be a good mother? How to explain to a social worker that you consider it important to be there emotionally for your child, always there, but that doesn't necessarily mean always physically there?

'You want too much,' says Izzy. 'You're too greedy for life.'

And I look at Sam and his castle and his halo of blond hair and I
think, Is that so wrong?

5

It is 16 August. A Friday. Julia has Sam and I have Mr James Baboneau. When do doctors cease to be Dr and elevate themselves to Mr? I go into the house, and it is a house and not a surgery, and report to Fiona, Baboneau's glowingly cheerful secretary.

'First-floor waiting-room,' she beams.

It's not as though I don't know. I've been here often enough.

'Thanks,' I say anyway. I think I'd say 'Thanks' if someone said, 'This is the electric chair.'

The sweep of the stairs is almost Jacobean. There is wood panelling and apricot wallpaper. The waiting-room is a gentle green, the chairs rosewood and the magazines country and county. I get out my book, though I know I will be called immediately. There is no one else here. This is private medicine.

'Hello! Come in!' At 9.30 precisely, Baboneau's door flies open. He smiles and gestures but he does not look at me.

I go in and sit down on the upright chair positioned a wide desk's space from his upholstered leather chair. I get out my list. Baboneau inspects his notes.

'How are you?' he asks.

'Not pregnant.'

I always give this reply and Baboneau always reacts as if I have said something brutal or distasteful. It's as though he thinks we should first discuss an uncontroversial topic: life, art, the weather, the waiting-room magazines. But this chair costs £55 for fifteen minutes (ten minutes if you deduct my crying time) and there are so many things, important things, I need to know.

'Do you have a job?' That's what Baboneau asked me the first time I ever came here, over a year ago. Asked as though a job would stop me fretting.

Today he gets to the point.

'The sperm test,' he says.

Now he does look at me. He leans forward, he puts his elbows on the table.

'Your husband', he says, and his smile is very broad, very masculine, 'has four times as much sperm as a not very well-endowed man. And twice the amount of an average man. His motility is excellent and his proportion of abnormal sperms indescribably low.'

I burst into tears.

'That's the good news,' he says, slightly bewildered.

I blow my nose.

'So it's still all my fault,' I say.

'Why do you have to look at it in terms of fault?' he asks. 'It's not productive.'

'Nothing seems to be productive.'

'Except your husband,' he jokes.

It's not so much bedside manner with Baboneau as bed of nails.

'Being a gynaecologist and being a man,' I say, 'must be rather like reading about America, but never actually getting to go there.'

'I'm sorry?' he says.

But he isn't.

Next we talk about the post-coital.

'Not a great success, was it? Are you having problems with sex?'

'None that conceiving a baby wouldn't cure.'

'What's your husband's reaction?'

'He likes fucking. Normally.'

'And now?'

'For God's sake, he's not a dog! Not a goat!' I add, looking at the glorious sperm test results.

'I think we ought to change the drug,' Baboneau decides. 'The negative test result, post-coital test that is,' he clarifies, 'suggests that the Clomid has thickened the mucus. After all, something must be impeding the passage of forty million sperms!'

Luckily, for him, he manages to suppress the laugh.

'So I suggest,' he continues, 'we try a little Rehibin.'

'Does it have any side-effects?' I ask.

'Like what?'

'Like getting pregnant, for instance.'

'What is it you do for a job?' he inquires. 'I forget.'

'I'm a comedian,' I tell him.

'Surely,' he says, 'you mean a comedienne?'

I remember, to comfort myself, the words of my friend Dr Susan Burns: 'Gynaecology is dull. Dull, dull, dull. Real dead-end stuff.' That's why, says Dr Burns, it attracts so few women.

£55 later, I leave. I'm clutching another prescription. The insurance doesn't pay for the drugs. I make another appointment, three months hence.

'When I first came here,' I tell Fiona, 'he said I'd be pregnant within six months. Do you think I'm due my money back?' I'm laughing. When Baboneau first mentioned the six months, a year ago, I didn't laugh. It seemed a lifetime to wait. Now of course, it seems such a small, such a desirable, time.

I walk home. On my doormat I find a letter from Izzy.

'Dearest Kate,' she writes, 'I'm making an apple pie! I just had to tell someone. My apple pie, my wonderful apple pie (I've even made pastry!) is all for me. No one else is here. But I felt I must share it. I've got an egg-cup upturned in the middle, pierced a hole between its feet. Jean would die. No open-throated blackbirds in this flat. But you should smell it, Kate. I peeled and cored all the apples myself. With a knife. And no, don't worry, I'm not going to turn into a caterer after all. But Kate, have you ever made an apple pie? It's so – real! And the smell. Boy, you should smell it. And after twenty minutes it won't exist any more. Except here in your letter. You're so privileged! I never made an apple pie for Martin.'

I fold the letter without turning the page and take the car keys from the dresser. The newness of apple pies and of train tunnels. Is it only me who's grown old?

6

We return from the Saturday shop at 12.30. Paul's pockets are lighter, Sam's heavier. He has a pack of bribery sweets. As usual we can't park outside our own house. Paul brakes, swears and puts on the emergency lights.

'Look!' shouts Sam, his mouth full of Black Jack.

Reclining on the low wall that borders the tile pathway to our door is a small figure, face upturned to the sun.

'Izzy! Izzy!' Sam bangs his fist on the window.

Izzy stirs as the car doors slam. She's dark and smaller than me, perennially the little sister. What if she'd been bigger, would it have changed our relationship? She gets up, smiles and trips over her rucksack as she comes to greet me.

We hug.

'Did you call?' I ask. 'Did you say you were coming?'

'No,' she says surprised. 'Did I have to?'

'What if we'd been away?'

'But you're not away.'

Her smile is sunshine.

'But if we had been!' I persist, inflexible, in a rut, habitual as my mother.

'I'd have gone to the beach.' She says this as though it's obvious, as though I'm mad.

'I haven't got any food in,' I accuse her peevishly.

Izzy looks at the piled, shopping-bagged car.

'You kidding?'

'Only two pieces of fish. Two chicken bits.'

'No hassle,' says Izzy. 'I'll get takeaway.'

Raid the freezer, she means.

'Izzy! Izzy!' Sam has been released from his seat. 'I've got a new gun. Come on!' He takes her hand, rings our door bell.

35

'Hi, Izzy.' Paul kisses her lightly. 'Been waiting long?' His smile is amused, tolerant.

'Come on!' insists Sam.

Paul unlocks the door and we all go in.

'Look!' Sam drags Izzy into the playroom. 'Playroom' is a rather grandiose title for this box room which abuts the kitchen. When the house was built it was probably a store-room, with boiler and walk-in larder. Now the pantry-shelves are full of books and games and toys (some too high for Sam to reach) and otherwise there is room for not much more than a small, spongey sofa, a television set, a chair and the old umbrella stand from which Sam's arsenal bristles.

'I just want a word with Mummy,' says Izzy.

'No,' wails Sam, pulling on his breastplate and his centurion's helmet and searching frantically for his matching grey sword.

Izzy leans out of the doorway and looks down the steps into the kitchen where I am unpacking apple juice and salami and fig rolls.

'I thought weapons were off,' she says. 'I thought this was a pacifist household.'

'One of the worst things about being a mother,' I tell her, 'is having one's theoretical hopes dashed.'

'What?'

'Accepting biological difference. Coming to terms with the fact that boys really will be boys. That they are fundamentally different. Alien. Programmed to kill.'

'And environmental conditioning?' says Izzy, shocked. 'And principles?'

'Mumm-Ra!' shouts Sam and digs her in the ribs with a battery-operated dagger. 'You're a witch! You're a slimer!'

'All went out the window the day Sam found my Kenwood mincer attachment and decided it was a ray-gun. As his vocabulary at the time was otherwise confined to dog, cat and biscuit, and Paul and I had never so much as mentioned a gun let alone bought one, I capitulated. It seemed easier.'

'Television,' says Izzy disapprovingly and then, 'Gotcha, you wretch!' and she wrestles Sam to the ground.

'Girls watch telly,' I say to the rollmops and the decaffeinated coffee and the oven chips. 'His little friend Charmian still doesn't know a trigger from a gun-barrel. And what's more she doesn't care.'

'Mum! Mum!' screams Sam. 'Help me!'

'You weed!' exclaims Izzy.

'Now would you say that to a girl?' I inquire. 'A little reflex is a dangerous thing.'

'What's for lunch?' asks Paul.

'Whatever you're making.'

I go upstairs in search of sheets for the spare room bed. Izzy follows me.

'Don't bother with that,' she says, 'I'll use the dirties.'

'There aren't any. The bed's stripped.'

I find a pink sheet and blue striped duvet cover.

'For God's sake!'

'What?'

'Where the hell is the pink cover?'

'Kate, when I'm asleep I won't notice the colour of the duvet.'

'You're so bloody young,' I inform her.

She waits, holding the blue cover.

'I keep meaning to tidy the airing cupboard,' I explain. But that sounds even more suburban. 'Oh, what the hell! Blue's great. I love blue.' Bravely I follow her into the spare room.

We stand either side of the double bed, joined by the cover. We lift the duvet and begin to pile it inside. Paul and I have a method: duvet into bottom corner, hold corner, push rest of duvet in, locate top corner, hold, wait till partner's ready, shake. The shake is very important. Button or popper. Final shake. Lay on bed.

Izzy is not paying attention. Not holding her corner. I'm ready to shake. But her half is a mess, rucked up, fucked up.

'Hold the bloody corner,' I shriek.

'What?'

'The corner. The corner! Don't you know how to do a fucking duvet?'

'I didn't know there was a way.'

I fling the duvet, rumpled and mountainous, on to the bed.

'Oh what's the point!'

'Hey, Kate!'

I sit down with my back to her.

'Kate?'

I am shaking with anger.

'What did I do?'

'Nothing, you stupid bitch.' My tears are tears of anger.

She sits down beside me.

'What is it?'

'Nothing,' I say. 'Everything.'

Then she puts her arms round me.

From the stairs, Sam calls.

After supper – and of course I diced and divided the chicken and added extra vegetables and rice and of course there was enough – Paul says, 'I'm afraid I have some reading to do, so if you ladies will excuse me...'

'Does he always work on a Saturday night?' asks Izzy.

'No.' This I love about Paul. He is taking himself away so that Izzy and I may be, at last, alone. I pour myself another glass of red wine. I've already had half a bottle. Drinking too much, and I am drinking too much these days, is bad for conception. But I've given up cigarettes and I'm not giving up booze. I need to drink sometimes. What else is there? Besides, children are born to alcoholics so it can't inhibit conception that much.

'What are you thinking?' asks Izzy.

'About God,' I say.

'Huh?'

'When I was pregnant with Sam I wrote to Phillida in New York, I wrote: "My conceiving Sam so quickly proves that God does not exist. If He did, He would have made me wait a very long time, so that the only thing I'd have wanted in the whole world was a child."' I quote verbatim. I wrote the letter at work and I still have it on disc. Sometimes I look it up, just to check on the person I was, her foolishness. Her hubris.

'God's not like that,' says Izzy.

'Like what?'

'Punishing.'

'Oh, really.' I look at her. She believes. This is one of the few things we have ever really argued about. There was a time, when Martin and God were both around, that I felt a little pushed out.

'You remember', I say, 'that... that discussion we had once, where I tried to persuade you out of God?'

'Very clearly.'

'When I said God didn't solve anything, only gave it name and made you think you had the answer...'

'I remember.'

'Well, I think He blames me for that too.'

'If He doesn't exist,' says Izzy, 'He can't blame you.'

'Precisely.'

There is a pause.

'What is hard to believe,' says Izzy, 'is that it's such a little time

38

since we were sitting here discussing what impact Sam might make on your life. How fearful you were. How terrified you were that he would interfere with your relationship with Paul. And with your professional, your "real" life.'

'The bigger they are the harder they fall.'

'Oh, rot.'

'I wrote that in the letter to Phillida too. How I didn't want anything to rock my life's boat. Only I actually wrote "lifeboat", I didn't want anything to rock my lifeboat. What do you make of that, Freud?'

One of the candles is guttering. Izzy digs a fingernail into its rim, snaking a channel for the escaping wax. She watches the liquid run red over the silver candlestick.

'Pretty ironic, that's what.' I take a fingerful of the soft wax, let it harden into my fingerprint and then chip it into pieces with my nails. Paul can't stand wax fiddlers. 'A decade of moaning about what a bum deal women get, and how babies are God's way of ensuring that we never get to the top, or get to stay at the top . . .'

'I thought we were leaving God out of this.'

'And then – wham bang thank you ma'am. I get to be thirty-five and think that if only I had a second child everything would be perfect. My life in perfect balance. Some time to work. Some time to mother. Some time for myself.'

'Do you get any time for yourself?'

'Some. More than Paul does. That's the point. Being thirty-five and a woman is, or could be anyway, so much better than being thirty-five and a man. I mean, what's Paul got? A nine-to-five stretching out to retirement. A child growing up almost despite him. Suddenly the joke seems to be on men after all. Why don't they notice, Izzy? I keep thinking Paul'll finally wake up at fifty and think, why did I do it? Surely there must be something else? Something more?'

'Do you ever say as much?'

'Course. But he doesn't seem to grasp the point. Or else he just accepts it as his lot. I'm not quite sure which. Why don't men ever complain, Izzy? About the big things?'

'Paul's not all men,' states Izzy.

'You think men of your generation are different?'

'Maybe.'

'That you're different?'

'Maybe.'

'You're just young. Full of possibilities. In front of you are millions of doors and you can take any one of them. And if you go through one door, and it's not the right door, you can turn back. Try another door and lose nothing. But as you get older every door you open seems to close another one you might have gone through but didn't. And some of the doors don't have inside handles. You can't go back. Your escape routes get cut off. Your mistakes begin to cost you, confine you. Sometimes I think I'll finally end up in a corridor where there aren't any doors at all.'

'I've never heard you talk like this before.'

'Like what?'

'Depressed.'

'Oh, tell me about it. And envious. Did you notice the envy? Your spontaneity makes me sick! Your ability to go with the flow. To arrive unannounced, unexpected. To let the day shape itself. Whether we were in or out. Doesn't matter. Don't care.'

'Is that what the duvet was about?'

'Maybe. Partly. You made me feel old. Boring. Ossified.' I look at her, my most beloved sister. 'Pathetic, isn't it?'

'No,' Izzy says solidly.

'Not to mention illumining the lovely self-pitying pit I've thrown myself into. Which makes me feel really terrific.'

Izzy stretches her hand towards me.

'Can a person give a person a pull out?'

'No.' I sound defensive, fierce. 'That's the point. The only person who can pull me out is me. Only I can't pull me out because I'm too far in and there aren't any hand-holds.'

Izzy touches my hand, strokes it.

I pull away a little.

'You remember when you phoned a few weeks ago and I said I couldn't talk because I had white sauce on the stove? And you said couldn't Paul stir the sauce? That was a revelation. Why couldn't he! Why didn't I think of it? Why did I think I owed it to him to stir the white sauce? We had a terrible row.'

'About the sauce?'

'About the fact that I was right. When I put it to him, he made it quite clear that being asked to stir the sauce so I could natter on the phone would have been wholly unacceptable.'

'We wouldn't have nattered,' says Izzy. 'We'd have talked.'

Suddenly I don't want to go on. This conversation is making me feel very vulnerable. Normally with Izzy it's me doing the hand-holding. Me the matriarch.

'Let's talk about you for a bit,' I say. 'I don't want to add selfishness to my list of crimes.'

40

'It's always more interesting talking about other people,' Izzy says. 'Listening to them.'

'I'm not other people,' I resist. 'Anyway fair's fair. By that token it's more interesting for me to listen to you.'

'*Touché*! OK. What do you want to know?'

'Everything. Anything. Life without Martin. How the job search is going.'

'You know about Martin. I wrote you. It's lonely. It's wonderful. I write more poems.'

'Good poems?'

'I doubt it. Just little pieces of solidification. Making my life real to myself, as telling him about it used to make it real.'

I nod. I know it is the sharing of the little things that binds my life to Paul's. I try to remember this when I feel so angry at him about the big things.

'And on the job front,' Izzy says, 'I'm going to Edinburgh, then doing the teaching for a bit and then I'll see. It doesn't seem that important.'

'It will when it's October and you've nothing to do.'

'Something will turn up.'

'You can't run a life like that.'

'Why not? And anyway, who said I wanted to run my life? Maybe I just want to respond to it. Be alert. Open. Available for whatever opportunities present themselves. Listen a bit. People don't listen enough.'

'You're supposed to be a child of the Thatcher decade. You're supposed to be go-getting.'

'I once met a man on a park bench. Blue eyes. Amazing smile. Said all the best things in his life had happened by coincidence. I thought about that a lot. It's true.'

'Not in my life.'

'What about meeting Paul?'

'I engineered that! Spotted him. Walked across the lawn. Sat down beside him. I made that happen!'

'But what if he hadn't been sitting under the tree that day?'

'Oh, Izzy!'

'No, think about it, Kate. You were open, available. You responded.'

'OK. Chance and planning, maybe. But not just chance! You have to take control of your life. That's what being grown-up means.'

'Who wants to be grown-up?'

'Oh, Izzy!'

41

'Stop "oh Izzying" me! I'm serious. In the Middle Ages it wouldn't have been grown-up to control things. Nobody controlled things.'

'Except God and nature and Mistress Chance.'

'Exactly. And we've lost all that. Think we can do it all. Well, maybe we can't.'

'Do you mean "shouldn't"?'

'Maybe. Maybe we'd be happier if we didn't try.'

'You'd be happier. Not trying doesn't suit my temperament.'

'Ease up, Kate. Give yourself a break!'

'Exactly!' says Paul, appearing suddenly at the top of the steps. 'That's what I'm always telling her. Ease up a bit. Get some exercise.'

'Exercise?' queries Izzy.

'Exercise,' says Paul. 'It blows away the cobwebs.'

He smiles, deposits a kiss on the top of my head and then he goes to bed.

'Do you know,' I tell Izzy, 'Paul's always asking me what I'm thinking. Especially in the car. And I'm always thinking about six things simultaneously. But when I asked him the same question once, do you know what he said? He said, "Nothing"!'

'Nothing!'

'Yuh. "I'm not thinking about anything"! Can you imagine thinking nothing, Izzy?'

'Your husband', says Izzy, 'is weird.'

There's a pause.

'And you know what "weird" means?' I challenge Izzy. I've done Old English too.

'Fate,' she says. 'My weirding sister.'

And the witch cackles.

7

Eleanor, James, Thomas, Rose, William, Georgina, Lucy, Alexander, Edward and Flora.

'Why are you reading yesterday's paper?' Paul asks.

'I'm checking on the population explosion.' The babies in Saturday's *Times* are, I've noticed, more numerous and more conventional than those in the weekday *Independent*.

It's Sunday evening. Izzy has gone and she's left a gap. Paul is ironing a shirt, readying himself for the week ahead. In a moment I shall go upstairs and pack my briefcase, search out a black biro and a 2B pencil, ensure I have my ArtsAid address book, choose a novel for the journey.

'On Wednesday,' Paul says, flipping over his shirt and folding it with a tailor's precision, 'I may have to go to Edinburgh.'

'What!'

'If they'll let me I'll take the sleeper on Tuesday night. Otherwise I'll have to drive.'

His tone is utterly reasonable, unperturbed. I don't think he's faking.

'You tell me,' I say, 'at ten o'clock, Sunday night, that you might be going to Edinburgh on Tuesday?'

'Or Wednesday,' he says, beginning a new shirt. White with thin red stripes.

'Or Wednesday. Well, that's just brilliant. Really brilliant. Thanks a lot, Paul.'

'What's the problem?' He up-ends the iron and there's a hiss of steam.

'The problem! Oh, for Christ's sake!' I fling Eleanor, James, Thomas, Rose, William, Georgina, Lucy, Alexander, Edward and Flora on to the floor.

'I would have told you earlier,' he says, 'but we had Izzy here and anyway, like I said, it may never happen.' He resumes ironing. 'The American guy I really need to see may or may not be arriving.'

'Do you know what Tuesday is?' I challenge him.

He considers a moment. 'Your birthday?'

'Oh, very funny. Hilarious. It's all just one big joke to you, isn't it?'

'Look, I have to work. I have bills to pay. We have bills to pay. And if that involves me visiting academics in Edinburgh on Wednesday and Thursday – then so be it!'

'Thursday!' I scream.

'Yes, Thursday. Only Thursday will probably be Glasgow.'

I pick up the paper. I put my fist through James. I tear Eleanor to shreds.

'What on earth is the matter with you?'

'What's the matter with me? What's the matter with you! Tuesday is Day 12. Thursday is Day 14!'

'Oh.'

I look at his face. He hasn't remembered. He didn't know.

'On Days 12 and 14,' I remind him, shouting, 'we are supposed to fuck. But you don't care about another child, do you? You don't give a damn. All you care about is signing up another book for your fucking stupid Ancient History List!'

'I'm not responsible', he says, his face going white and hard round the edges, 'for the travel arrangements of Professor Hayden Lewis.'

'No. Course not. But you are responsible for your own life!'

'What's that supposed to mean?'

'You didn't even know it was Day 14, did you?'

'I don't think it helps to know,' he says. 'We didn't know anything about days when we conceived Sam. If it's going to happen, it'll happen.'

'Not if you're in fucking Glasgow it won't.'

He folds the red and white shirt. He now has five neatly pressed shirts. Enough for the week, for his going-away bag. He switches off the iron.

'Come on, Kate,' he says, 'let's go to bed.'

'Why?' I say. 'What's the point?'

And so I put paid to any hope of us making love tonight.

'Day 10', says Mr James Baboneau, 'is a little early for optimum fertility, but someone in your position should really have it covered.'

My Day 10 position is back to back.

Naturally, Professor Lewis arrives and Paul departs.

44

I really would like not to know about the days. But what am I to do? On Day 1, I start my period. Can I forget five days of blood? On Day 4 (or 6 depending on the drug) I start taking the pills. I have to know the days, or I may start the course too early, too late, and then what would be the point at all? The drugs normally stop by Day 9. Now I must test the mucus. The surest sign of ovulation is the change from milky white to saliva clear. Some women have no such obvious thinning and yet ovulate perfectly normally. Sometimes I think I'm one of these women. Sometimes I think there is no change because I'm not ovulating. But the blood tests say I'm ovulating. Some women have blood, or pain on ovulation. Not me. I envy them these definite, outward signs. But I still wait and watch for the two or three days when fertilization could occur – four or five days if you count the length of time a sperm may be able to survive in the tubal fluids. Forty-eight hours or more, according to some research. Paul says I read too much. Know too much. But what am I to do? I appear to have so little control that I grasp for that I can have.

On Day 14 the Samson pamphlet arrives. It comes in a small brown envelope hand-addressed to Mr K. Francis. It comes, apparently, from Chick Publications, California, or else Evangelistic Literature Enterprise, Queensland, or else Christ is the Answer, Inc. of Canada. These and other addresses are listed on the back. The postmark on the envelope is Sheffield. I know no one in Sheffield. Considering the 'Mr', maybe no one knows me.

Except God, who knows it's Day 14.

Izzy knows it's Day 14 too. But this is not Izzy's sort of joke. Nor is it her hand. The writing is open, generous, middle-aged. On the back of the booklet, in a white box labelled 'Compliments of', my anonymous benefactor has penned: 'God bless you, dear friend. Numbers 6; 24, 25, 26.'

Of course I should take no notice, throw the wretched little comic into the bin. But I'm still marvelling at it when Tessa arrives at nine o'clock. If she's going to arrive at all, Tessa is extremely punctual. I'm grateful for this.

'Hello, darling,' she shouts at Sam as she passes the playroom. I hear him sink deeper into the sofa. She comes into the kitchen, dumps her bag on the table and plops into the chair opposite me.

'Whatcha reading?' she asks, getting out her mirror and rearranging her lips and hair.

'The bloody tale of Samson,' I inform her, 'who slaughtered many more people than he got credit for in my school but not half so many as God's apparently going to slaughter at a later date.'

'What?' says Tessa.

' "Unlike Samson",' I quote, ' "Jesus Christ will slaughter billions of people at His second coming. All who oppose Him will be smashed. He will take over this world and rule from Jerusalem as King of kings and Lord of lords." The only way to be on the winning side, Tessa, is to choose Christ as your God. So, do you want to rule with Christ when you die or be with Satan in the lake of fire? Ten seconds, starting now.'

'That's rubbish,' says Tessa. 'What do you want to read that for?'

Tessa has a large, tough face and short blonded hair. I bet Samson wouldn't have got past her the day he mauled the lion.

'I'm reading it because it's here,' I say. 'And because I'm seeking desperate answers to desperate questions.' At first I told Tessa nothing of my 'subfertility' but, as Sam's friends began to acquire brothers and sisters, her inquiries became increasingly, irresistibly direct.

'You know what I think?' she says now, snapping shut her compact.

'What?'

'I think you don't know how to do it.'

This is a departure even for Tessa. I check her face to see if I've heard correctly.

Her face is perfectly painted, perfectly composed. Almost vacant. It's true. Tessa thinks her employer and her employer's husband, who have a three-year-old child, do not know how to fuck. For her it is not an accusation, but a statement of fact. The stupidity, rudeness or simple hurtfulness of the remark do not concern her. Such is the beauty of truth.

I observe my watch.

'I must get on,' I remark and I stand up with my half-finished mug of coffee in one hand and the Samson pamphlet in the other. 'See you, Tessa.' As I pass the playroom, I alert Sam to my departure.

'Don't go,' he says, but his eyes are on the video.

'See you at lunch.'

I go upstairs to the study. I'd like every book in here, every piece of paper and every pencil to belong to me as the desk and the cheap computer belong to me. But this is also Paul's room. It's here that he keeps his grandfather's inkstand, his jaguar paperweight, his carefully arranged classical texts, his slim, alphabetically ordered, volumes of modern poetry. When Paul works in here he begins by tidying all my 'bits' (my personal correspondence, my leaflets, my bank statements,

my newspaper cuttings, my ArtsAid papers) into my in-tray. I begin
by taking them all out again and spreading them over the desk.

Not today. Today I look for a bible. I must have had one. Paul must
have had one. His will be easier to find. It will sit by the reference
books, by Liddell and Scott's Greek-English Lexicon, by Harrap's
Concise, by Crabbe's English Synonyms. Yes, here it is.

I look up Numbers 6; 24, 25, 26:

24: On the third day Eliab the son of Helon, prince of the children
of Zebulun, did offer:
25: His offering was one silver charger, the weight whereof was an
hundred and thirty shekels, one silver bowl of seventy shekels, after
the shekel of the sanctuary; both of them full of fine flour mingled
with oil for a meat offering:
26: One golden spoon of ten shekels, full of incense:

I read on. These are apparently peace offerings. Is this the point?
Have I to make peace with my wrathful God? Give money to the
church or perhaps give more, something of myself? Must I believe?
Or am I just holding in my hands the religious equivalent of a
horoscope, with me working to fit its prophecies into the knowledge of
my life? The paper is bullying me. (Respond, says Izzy, respond.) I do
not like to feel bullied. I do not like this savage pamphlet with its filthy
lucre commands. I will not be fooled, be called to account by a
slaughtering God or a stranger in Sheffield. I will not be shot in the
dark, in the back. I am about to tear the booklet in two and cast it away,
when I see I have read the wrong chapter. I have read Numbers 7. I
flip a thin bible page backwards to Numbers 6; 24, 25, 26:

24: The Lord bless thee, and keep thee:
25: The Lord make his face shine upon thee, and be gracious unto
thee:
26: The Lord lift up his countenance upon thee and give thee
peace.

And all at once I want my God and his shining mercy. I want to be
blessed and held, kept close and comforted. I want to be given the
peace I cannot give myself. Peace from the inside of my own head.
Peace from my want of a child. God's child. But I haven't paid the
price. Refused to pay it.

I am unshriven.

I go to bed early and lie alone between the white sheets.

Part of me is glad.

Tonight there can be no row, no failure. Infertility has destroyed my ability to seduce. I want to make love with my head, but my heart and my body are cold. I feel each fold of my flesh as ugly and my desire is lumpen. Paul, who has stroked and loved each tiny part of me, Paul is not fooled. My deadened sex cannot ignite him. He too goes through the motions, and our lovemaking is a sham; quick, angry and unfulfilling. Our orgasms are tight and release us only from duty.

Afterwards he sleeps and I lie awake. I feel as if I don't love him and the thought of not loving him makes me want to cry.

On Friday morning Paul rings to say he loves me and have I remembered that the plumber is coming to fix the shower?

I have remembered.

'I'll be back tonight,' he says, 'but don't wait up.'

His last appointment is 4.30 and then there is a six-hour drive. With breaks he reckons on being home between midnight and 1 a.m.

'Drive safely,' I tell him.

'Have you missed me?'

'Yes.'

'I've missed you. And my little boy.' There is a sudden warmth and youthfulness in his voice. I remember the calls we had when we were students. I remember that I have known and loved this man for over half my lifetime.

'Drive safely,' I say again.

'I will.'

The day is hot and long. The plumber, who is scheduled to come at 11.30 a.m., arrives at 3.30 p.m.

'Do you know,' I ask him, 'what it's like being confined to your house on a day like this? With a three-year-old?'

'Job ran on.' He shrugs. 'Didn't they call you?'

Of course they didn't. They never do.

'What's your name?'

'Mike.'

I make Mike a cup of tea. Can I trust Mike? Can I go out and leave him to it?

'Park,' says Sam, '*now*!'

I decide that as we know Petts Plumbing well, if not this particular employee, it's safe to go out. Besides, Paul need never know.

48

When we return an hour and a half later, Mike has gone. The bill on the kitchen table is addressed to Mrs Gregory. Kate Francis booked the plumber, Kate Francis waited in for him but it's Paul Gregory's name that usually appears at the bottom of the cheques. I decide not to let it bother me.

At 7.30 p.m. I let it bother me. There is water dripping down the flex of my hall light and splashing off the light bulb on to the floor below. I go upstairs to the airing cupboard and check the amended pipework. Mike, it seems, has put in a new stopcock which is leaking at the joint. If I turn the little red wheel, it'll shut off the water supply. Won't it? What if the wheel controls something else entirely and turning it off precipitates a build-up (of what? of water?) and then the pressure (will there be pressure?) causes an explosion? I take a chance. I shut down the red wheel. Nothing. The water keeps on dripping. I turn the tap back on. It seems safer that way. Then I go downstairs for a saucepan. The saucepan is too big to fit under the tap. I go downstairs again and return with a cereal bowl.

Then I ring Petts Plumbing. They operate a twenty-four-hour emergency service. There is no answer from the phone. I replace the handset and dial again. Still no answer.

I go outside, lift the man-hole cover, and turn off the mains water supply. So much for my much-needed bath. Nevertheless, I go upstairs again with a small sense of triumph. I look in the cereal bowl. It's filling with water. Still. Drip, drip, drip. I turn off the red tap. Drip, drip, drip. I turn on the red tap.

Fuck the tap. I ring Petts. No answer.

I ring another twenty-four-hour plumber. A woman asks if she can have my number, she'll get someone to call me back. I give her my number and, half a cereal bowl later, someone calls me back. It's Ted. Ted says he's got another job lined up and he lives in Horsham. He could be with me by 10 p.m. probably.

'Or midnight,' I say.

'What?'

'Just tell me,' I say, 'is it OK to turn the little red wheel on the stopcock?'

'Gate-valve,' he says.

'What?'

'Not a stopcock, a gate-valve.'

'Fine. Is it OK to shut off the gate-valve?'

'Should be.'

'Shouldn't that shut off the water?'

'Yeah. Should do.'

49

'Then why isn't it?'

'Can't say without looking. Might be something simple. Might need to drain down the system.'

'What if it is just something very simple? You turn off a tap. How much does it cost me?'

'£50.'

'Can I take your number and call you?'

'No. I'm not allowed to give you my number.'

What a surprise.

'OK. I'll call the office.' I put down the phone. What are the chances of Petts refunding me the £50? Nil. What are the chances of Petts answering their own twenty-four-hour phone? Nil. Apparently.

I go upstairs, collect and empty the cereal bowl, replace it under the tap. If there was room for a bigger bowl I could let the tap leak all night. But there isn't room. How can it be leaking anyway when the mains water is off? How can I know so little about how my water system works? How come I'm so useless? I comfort myself that, even if Paul were here, he wouldn't know any more than I do. But he might. I ring his hotel.

'I'm sorry, Mr Gregory checked out at 6 p.m.'

He's on his way then. That's something, anyway.

I ring Petts. Nothing.

I ring a second twenty-four-hour plumber. Their call-out fee is £45. It's beginning to sound cheap.

'I'll call you back,' I say.

I ring my Dad. Not that he's much of a DIY man.

'Hello, you have reached Complete Catering. We're sorry there is no one here to take your call right now, but whatever your catering needs, large or small, Derek and Jean Francis look forward to receiving your message after the tone. Just leave your name and number and please speak clearly ... *beeeep*.'

'Hi. It's me. Could you do me a doughball big enough to swamp a leaking stopcock? Not to mention a gate-valve? Thanks. Bye.'

This gives me an idea. Didn't Paul buy some waterproof tape? I look in the cupboard under the stairs. Paul is not much of a DIY man either but his tools and equipment, such as they are, are neatly ordered. Tapes have a shelf to themselves. Masking tape. Electrical tape. Sticky parcel tape. And yes ... *yes*! Waterproof tape! Paul bought it for a drainpipe. The seal on the box is unbroken. I carry my treasure to the airing cupboard. The tape is khaki. A loose bandage-type mesh impregnated with a thick gluey substance that comes off on your fingers like snot. I read the instructions. The tape contains petroleum jelly. The use of a barrier cream is recommended. Use the tape in spirals.

I use it in spirals. I wind the tape around and around the pipe. I smooth the snot over the cracks. My fingers suck and stick. But soon, very soon, the flow of water will be stemmed. The tape will triumph. I will triumph. I cut the tape, squeeze down the last join. I sit back to look at my work. I wait. Slowly, almost imperceptibly, the tape glazes. It glistens. Then the flat sheen rises, it bubbles, a drop forms and it slides, stickily, down the tape and into the waiting cereal bowl. Then another. And another.

I want to scream. If Sam wasn't asleep across the landing I would scream. Instead, I take the tape downstairs and go into the kitchen to wash my hands. The water runs off my palms, off my fingers. My hands are waterproofed.

'Aargh!'

I get kitchen roll. I wipe and pull the snot off my hands. It smears. I get white spirit. It thins and smears. I wash and wash. I use Fairy Liquid. I use soap. I use water. The water runs off. It runs into the cereal bowl. It runs down my electrical wires. It runs out of my landing light and splashes off my light bulb on to the floor.

'Aargh! Aargh! Aargh!'

I get more kitchen paper and wrap it round the phone.

I ring Petts. No answer.

I ring Christian.

'Hello?'

'Christian,' I say, 'Christian, could you come round?'

When Christian arrives, my hands are clean and dry but my face is wet.

'You've been crying,' he says. 'What's up?'

'My shower pipe leaks,' I blub.

Christian looks at me, puts his arms round me.

'Must be one hell of a leak,' he says.

Christian is one of my oldest and dearest friends. He's intelligent, he's kind and he thinks like a woman.

'Come on now,' he says, 'show me.'

I take him upstairs. All the other gay men I know have small neat bodies. Christian is large and loose-limbed, the sort of man who inspires confidence because he looks so relaxed. His eyes are brown, his lashes far too long and he knows nothing about DIY. He can't even change a plug.

51

He observes the weeping pipe. I tell him about the gate-valve and the mains water and the possibility that the system may need 'draining down'.

'Aha.' He is looking upwards, following the pipe through the airing cupboard roof – to where? He opens the upper cupboard. There are two tanks. He gets a stool. Feels which tank the pipe joins.

'Cold water,' he says. 'Now let's suppose the pipe is being fed by the cold tank, that though the water is off the pipe will continue to leak for as long as there is water up here, above it. So, empty the tank and bingo! No leak!'

'You making it up?'

'Sure. But it's worth a go, surely?'

I'm on my way to get bailing saucepans when he says, 'We could always just turn on the cold tap in the bath.'

I turn on the cold tap in the bath. The water runs away. Because the mains is off the tank does not refill. The leak stops.

The leak stops.

I burst into tears.

'Now what is it really?' asks Christian.

'It is the leak,' I sob. 'It was the leak. And because I couldn't do anything about it. Couldn't stop it. I'm just so hopeless. So out of control. I can't even handle a leak!'

'You handled it,' says Christian, 'you tried everything and then you rang me. And I'd have tried everything you tried first, if you hadn't already tried it.'

We go downstairs. I take the kettle to make him coffee. There's no water.

'You might have thought of saving some water for coffee!' I say.

'I'll make do with wine.'

I open a bottle of Corbières. It's 9.30.

'Have you eaten?' I ask him.

'No.'

'Nor have I.' I look in our depressed fridge. 'Well, I can make you scraps or I can use the money I saved on the plumber to dial-a-pizza.'

'Dial away.'

The pizza people are home. They will bring us Four Seasons, deep pan, large, they'll be thrilled to do it. They'll be with us in twenty-five minutes.

They are with us in twenty-four minutes. I open a second bottle of wine.

'Friday night,' I inform Christian.

'Is Paul back tonight?'

'Yup.'

'And is that going to make you happier?'

'Probably not.'

Christian lifts his left eyebrow and gives me his quizzical, tell-me-about-it look.

'Same old thing,' I tell him merrily.

'No second child?'

Christian can be relied on to get to the point.

'No second child.'

He sits, eats pepperoni.

'Doesn't having Sam make it any better?' He looks at my face. 'A bit better?'

'No.' I've thought about this a lot. 'Actually, I think it makes it worse. Because it's the joy of Sam, the gift of him which makes me know what I'm missing.'

I see the sudden small withdrawal of Christian's lips which indicates a disapproval which he doesn't – yet – wish to articulate.

'I mean,' I spar him, 'nobody would say to a guy just about to have his left leg amputated, aren't you glad to have a right leg!'

'Not the same.'

'Oh no?'

Christian is concentrating on his pizza, avoiding my gaze now. 'My friend Jane', he says, 'has been trying to conceive for six years. She'd think one child a miracle.'

'Grass is greener. Man in concentration camp is so hungry he doesn't notice the cold. Gets a slice of bread and then realizes how frozen he is. I know all that comparative stuff, but it doesn't make it any better.' I pause. 'Do you understand that?'

'Not really.'

Christian, who understands everything.

'You know,' I say, 'sometimes I wish I had a friend Jane. My problem is that all my friends conceive like rabbits.'

'You make it sound like keeping-up-with-the-Joneses. I want. Gimme, gimme. Why should they have something I can't have?'

I feel a vinous tear coming. 'You mean I'm selfish?'

'I didn't say that. Though – well, what is your motive for wanting another child?'

'Motive! Does there have to be a motive?' Why is he pushing me? Doesn't he know, my Christian, that I want his face to shine upon me and give me peace? 'I mean, I could pretend bringing a child into this rotten world would be in the best interests of the child, but it wouldn't, probably. I mean, there isn't a good, non-selfish reason for having a child, is there? Somewhere along the line we all do it for ourselves. Immortality, fulfilment, biology, whatever.'

'OK. Sure. For a first child.'

'All right then, I want a second child for Sam. So he'll have a family. So he won't grow up almost like an only child, like I did for fourteen years. Pre-Izzy. Lonely. Goddam it, I was lonely!'

'*You* were lonely!'

'Yes, I was lonely. Me! Me! Me! Spoilt, spoilt spoilt!' I'm shouting a little. 'Do you know what's worse than not conceiving, Christian? It's behaving badly. Feeling guilty. Selfish! Yes – spoilt!'

Again Christian's lips move mutely: 'You're letting me down.'

'I'm confused,' I tell him. 'What is the agenda here, Christian?'

He pushes away his plate, his pizza half-eaten. And then all of a sudden I see him: this only child of distant parents, this gay man who will never have a child of his own.

'I'm sorry,' I say, 'is this about you?'

'How could it be?' he says.

Christian's homosexuality is known but taboo, the only unspoken subject that has ever lain between us. I have resented that, his openness with the emotions of others, his closedness for himself.

'How do you feel,' I ask him, carefully, fearfully, breaking a fifteen-year pact, 'about the possibility of not having a child yourself?'

'It's not relevant.'

'But how do you feel?'

'I don't think about it.'

He puts his knife and fork together, wipes his mouth and neatly balls his napkin. He drains his glass. I feel him going before he stands.

'I'm sorry,' I say.

'What for?'

For intruding, dear friend. For speaking the unspeakable. For asking you to open the box you have locked with such care. Asking you to feel because I can't stop feeling. Can't not think. Can't lock my hurt away.

'We're different,' I say. 'We deal with things differently.'

'I said I'd meet Nick at eleven,' he says. 'Thanks for supper.'

'Thanks for doing the leak.'

He kisses me and I wave him into the night.

Is my obsession to close doors on my friendships?

I decide to wait up for Paul. Day 15 is, after all, not so long after Day 14.

When midnight comes and goes, I phone Izzy.
'What's the justification for a second child?' I ask her.
'Sorry?'
'The reason for the desire?'
'Since when,' she says, 'do desires have to have reasons?'
My sister is a sphinx.

At 12.35 Paul arrives. He kisses me.
'I'm shattered,' he says.

8

In vitro fertilization is more successful when performed on Days 12 or
16. Remember that, says Mr James Baboneau, if you feel overly
concerned about Day 14.

I remember that. I alert Paul to the fact (not for the first time) on
Saturday afternoon. Day 16. He nods, acknowledging the early warning system. 'Tonight,' I'm telling him with my head, 'when I stretch
my lack-lustre hands towards your body, please respond.'

Later, in the dark, he responds. We perform. We also perform on
Day 17. Two nights running. A miracle. And so, despite the dubious
odds, I begin to hope again. This is how my lunar cycles turn. First
the blood and then the waiting, then the ovulation and the performance and then the waiting again, the hoping, the testing of mucus day
by day until the appearance of the first pink stain, the failure, the
misery and yet still the desperate hope, maybe this month just the
stain, quite common, but no real blood, please no real blood, no
period, a final wait, a long three days or four and then the sudden rush
of red, the vicious spilling of the womb. All this happening in my
body. No wonder Paul does not know which day it is.

In this Glasgow month I wait. I hope. On Day 24 the first pink
comes. I do not yet tell Paul. Instead I find my son.

'Do you want a brother or sister?' I ask him.

When I first asked him this question over a year ago, he answered,
'Just Mummy. Just Daddy. Just Sam.'

I was alarmed and astonished by his certainty. They say siblings
know, they say (the witches? the sphinxes?) that a sibling is never
wrong about the gender of a coming child. Or whether or if it comes?

Today Sam is building a Lego castle. Beneath its battlements is a
gaol where the good Black Knight will fling his red opponents.

'Yes,' says Sam.

'Yes! You would like a brother or sister?'

'Yes.'

56

'Which?'

'A plastic one.'

The Red Knight, *sans* his helmet, is incarcerated.

'Stay there, you baddie!' says Sam. 'You horror-bag! You witch!'

Four days later the red blood comes. I don't tell Paul at first. I go downstairs, I eat breakfast, I bath, I dress. I watch the way Paul ties his tie, his long fingers neat and exact. I go close to him, look at his work face.

'I got my period,' I say.

A flash of something lights his face. Anger, I think, but it's gone almost before I could say it was really there.

He leans towards me, kisses my forehead.

'Never mind,' he says, 'we'll try again next month.'

He takes his jacket, turns.

'Is that all you can say?'

He pauses and then I hear the sudden and impatient breath.

'What am I supposed to say?'

I want him to say it's as bitter for him as it is for me. I want him to embrace the pain, share it with me. I want to feel in this together. At the moment I feel it's my body, my guilt, my period, my problem. My pain.

'If you hurt more, I'd hurt less,' I tell him.

'We've been through all this, Kate.'

'And if you'd talk about it more, I'd need to talk about it less.'

'There's nothing to talk about. It'll happen. What else can I say?'

'When will it happen! If it hasn't happened for twenty months why should it ever happen again!'

There is another pause. I wait for him to say, 'This month wasn't a fair trial. I was away in Scotland at the crucial time. Next month will be different.'

'Do you know what I think you need?' he says.

'Exercise?'

'A holiday.'

'A holiday. A holiday!' I look at him. 'Do you really think it will happen again?'

'Yes, of course.'

'How can you be so certain?'

'Do you want me not to be certain? Do you want me to say, "It'll never happen again"?'

'I want you to tell me what you really think. Really feel.'

'I've told you. What's the point of saying everything seventeen times?'

57

'Because otherwise it just goes seventeen times round my head. Talking about it lets it out, makes it better.'

'It doesn't make it better.'

'Not for you, maybe, but for me.'

'And what about if talking about it makes it worse for me?' he says. 'Does it?'

'Yes. Yes. I've told you!'

'Why does it?'

Say because it makes you hurt, Paul, because it makes you hurt...

'Because there's no point. It doesn't change anything.'

'Oh, Paul.'

'Look, this isn't the time. I have to go to work.'

'It's never the time.'

'Book a holiday, Kate.'

'For God's sake, I don't need a holiday, Paul! I need a child!'

'You need something to take your mind off it. Book something. Anything. I have to go.'

He goes.

I go downstairs to Sam. It's Thursday, our day together. Sam is still in his pyjamas.

'Come here,' I say.

'Why?' he asks. But he comes.

I lift him on to my knees, I lean my head against his warm neck. He begins to pull away from me and then he hears the sob, huge and rolling.

'Mummy?' he says. 'Mummy?' And he clings to me, tiny and frightened. 'Mummy, what's the matter!'

'I want a new baby,' I sob against him.

A terrible noise rises in his throat, he clasps tighter and tighter and then he wails too, only his wail is chaos, pure empathy not understanding. My hurt hurts him so immediately, so directly that I am assuaged. And ashamed. I absorb another second of his holding and then I lift my head.

'I'm sorry,' I say, 'don't cry. I love you, Sam. Everything's OK. I love you, Sam. Mummy loves you.'

He looks at my face to see if I'm telling the truth. I wipe his tears and then mine. I smile at him. He makes me brave. He makes me ashamed. He is ineffably beautiful.

And my behaviour is, I know, unforgivable.

After lunch we go to the beach. Sam is insistent. It's a warm day and I fear there will still be crowds. But it's September now and the great British public seem suddenly in retreat, preparing behind closed doors for the autumn term, the winter, Christmas.

The pebbles have been washed into a high ridge from which vantage point I can scan the whole beach. I set out my towel and prepare for a minor boredom. I have brought a book but I do not expect to be able to read. I need to keep my eyes on Sam. He chooses a spot about ten yards from me and begins, rhythmically, to move stones. The activity is absorbing and, apparently, purposeless. He's muttering to himself. A boy about Sam's age skirts one of the pebble piles, watching and waiting. This is good. Sam is a social child and will probably invite the boy to play. This will treble the length of the game. I see, but cannot hear, Sam's first overture. The boy sits down. I open my book.

Without knowing that I am looking, I'm suddenly aware of a figure on the promenade behind me. It's a man pushing a pram and though he's too far away to see distinctly, I am convinced that it is Pippa's husband, Richard. Thursday is often a day Richard spends with Josh, but the likelihood of them being in Brighton is remote. They live in London. Yet still I'm sure, if for no better reason than the fact that the man is holding the pram with both hands. I always think this the sign of the committed father. Most men steer prams casually, with one hand, as if they weren't really doing it, as though mere accident connected them to the child, as though at any moment they might let go and never know the difference.

As the man comes nearer I focus harder. He has Richard's height and gait. He's tall and dark and has to stoop slightly to hold the pram. Soon I can distinguish the man's clean-angled face. Richard is classically handsome, square-jawed with beautifully spaced features. Not my type at all, but he turns heads. I see a head turn.

'Richard!' I shout. 'Richard!'

He stops, looks about him.

I check Sam's position and then race over the stones.

'Richard! What the hell are you doing here!'

'Hi, Kate.' He leans down to kiss me, then he nods at Josh. 'Just getting the bastard off to sleep.'

'Long way to come. Why didn't you tell me you were coming?'

'Didn't know myself till this morning.'

'Just a spontaneous day out for Josh?' I am incredulous. I think of Richard with his double first, his proficiency in five languages and his glittering career as a foreign correspondent, as the most meticulous of planners.

'No, not just for Josh. For me too. I needed to get out of the flat. I needed to think.'

'A glittering career *and* the ability to think with a one-year-old around. I'm really impressed.'

We lift the pram together, carrying the sleeping child over the stones. Richard positions the buggy carefully, back to the sea, shielding Josh's face from the sun. Sam comes over immediately. Having identified my spoils he returns to his stones. Josh is too young to be of interest and Richard is a man more entranced with his own child than with other people's.

'Don't have a glittering career any more,' he says as we sit.

'Oh no?' I'm surprised. 'Abandoning a national newspaper to write a book on The New Europe for Penguin at the same time as entering active fatherhood seems pretty glittering to me.'

'Desert Island Discs syndrome,' says Richard.

'What?'

'I hate that programme. I think it's the single biggest contributor to malcontent in this country.'

'Why!'

'All those people with seamlessly happy, seamlessly successful lives. All fake. They just put in the good bits and play music where the bad bits should be.'

'You mean you have bad bits at the moment?'

'Doesn't everyone?'

The thought that Richard's life might not be seamlessly successful is new to me. I turn the idea over in my mind and find it gives me a little glow, as if Richard's problems – whatever they are – somehow subtract from my own. I wish I didn't find myself to be so ungenerous.

'Do you want to talk about it?'

Richard picks up a stone and flings it – over the heads of the children – towards the sea. It falls short.

'I've got itchy feet.'

I wait, astonished, for some revelation about Pippa, but he continues in a torrent:

'I should never have turned down the *Independent*. I'm just not cut out to have my feet under a desk. I need to be flying about, seeing people, meeting deadlines. This book idea was madness. And looking after Josh too. I mean, he's wonderful, great, I'd lay down my life for him. But he's such a bloody tie. I feel so tied. And it's making me tongue-tied. The book's just ground to a halt. Can't think. Got no enthusiasm. No idea what comes next.'

'Get a full-time nanny,' I say, 'finish the book PDQ and offer yourself back to the paper with new-improved-published-book-author kudos. I'm sure they'd have you like a shot.'

He sighs. 'Oh, it's not really looking after Josh, I suppose. I mean my Mum does most of the work anyway. And Pippa's mother can't wait to take on more.'

'You think the paper wouldn't have you. That you burnt your boats?'

He huffs again. 'It's just that the job of foreign correspondent is not really compatible with a wife and two children.'

'*Two* children?' I inquire, as the sky goes dark.

'Yes, two. Pippa's pregnant again. Didn't she tell you?'

'No,' I say immediately. 'No.' My fingers are digging down, through the stones, into the wet grit of the beach beneath. 'Congratulations.'

'Oh, thanks,' he says derisively.

'I thought Pippa was against two kids,' I say. 'I thought she thought it ecologically unsound.'

'It was an accident.'

'An accident,' I repeat. The stone against my palm is jagged.

'But I think she's probably quite glad now. But that's not the point. Josh alone changes the stakes. I mean, I don't want to miss out on his growing up – but I'm just going to go crazy unless I can get away. And not just every so often. Regularly. It's like a fix.'

Josh smacks his one-year-old lips and begins to stir.

'What am I going to do, Kate?'

'God knows,' I say. I think my palm is bleeding. 'Don't ask me.'

When I get home I do not ring Pippa. I don't ring her over the weekend either, though I have plenty of business excuses. I see her for the first time in the office on Monday morning. I am quite calm, quite rational.

'Do you know', I scream at her, 'what's one worse than not conceiving? It's having your best friend hold out on you!'

'What?' she says, bewildered.

'Having your pal conceive and then finding out from a third party because she can't bring herself to tell you personally, just in case her joy might be your pain. For Christ's sake, Pippa, I'm glad you're pregnant. I'm thrilled. I really am. Congratulations! You bastard!'

Pippa stands up. She comes over to me.

'That stupid husband of mine,' she says, putting her arms round me. 'Of course I would have told you, Kate. But I'm only eight weeks. I haven't even told my parents yet.'

'Oh shit. I'm sorry.' I know I'm going to blub and I do.

Later I look at her. She's nearly forty, she's fertile, she's answering the telephone. I hope she miscarries.

9

At lunch Pippa says she's going to get a sandwich, do I want one?

'No thanks. I have to go out.'

'Oh?'

It's a fair question. I never go out at lunch, except to the market, and then we normally go together.

'Liaison,' I inform her, 'rendezvous with Fate.'

'Tell!' she demands.

'Impossible to know the unknowable,' I opine and then I leave.

I walk light-footedly through Soho. I am moving purposefully even though I do not yet know my final destination. It's a new experience for me. I look to right and left, seeing shops I've never noticed before and streets I've never turned down. I turn down them, as if by doing so I could step on to a different planet. I want to be on a different planet. But the buildings and the people are familiar, the territory still my own. I move faster, back street by back street, towards Oxford Circus. I'm waiting and searching. I'm confident. And there, finally, it is: a small shop-front with bright posters, peeling posters and exhortations handwritten in red. I go in.

There are two assistants, a man and a woman, both on the phone. I move casually, blind-man-buff style, towards the racks of brochures. I make one choice – European cities – and then I select at random. Or maybe not quite at random. The brochure I pick has a picture of Prague on the front. I've always wanted to go to Prague. I put myself and the brochure down in front of the man.

'Can I help?' he asks finally.

'I'd like to book a holiday, long weekend.'

He gets out a printed card and flourishes his pen over it.

'Where to?'

I open the Time Away brochure. They fly to Paris, Amsterdam, Venice, Florence, Rome, Madrid, Seville, Prague and Budapest.

'Don't care,' I say.

I see his lips tighten. He thinks I'm wasting his time.

'I'm easy,' I clarify. 'You choose. Whatever's available. Only not Venice. I've been there.' I want to add 'Madrid last and Prague first' but that wouldn't be playing the game.

The man chews his pen disdainfully.

'And do you mind when you go?'

'Any weekend in the next two months. Up to but not including 10 November. That's ArtsAid Day. Have you heard about ArtsAid Day?'

Unsurprisingly, he hasn't.

'I'll bring you a poster,' I offer.

'Hotel class?' he inquires.

'Three star. Two rather than four.'

This price limitation gives him a little confidence.

'Is it just for you?'

'And my husband.'

He begins to take our details.

'How about,' I say, 'I sign an Access form and you just fill it in when you've booked something?' If he knew me, he'd hear the wobble in my voice.

'Without consulting you about the choice?'

'Sure. You've got my phone number. Book it. Then ring and tell me what you've chosen.'

'You must be a hell of a ball at Christmas!' he says suddenly and he smiles.

I smile too. 'Sure am,' I tell him. 'I'm a wow for surprises!'

We conclude our deal.

He waves me out of the shop. It occurs to me (watching my Access form slip into his top drawer) that I could be waving goodbye to God knows how much to God knows who.

But mainly, I feel so spontaneous I could combust.

Later I ring my mother.

'Could you babysit, Jean? Sam will be at school by then and I'll ask Tessa to do extra hours so it would really only be Friday and Monday evenings, possibly Thursday and the weekend?'

'What weekend are we talking about, Kate?'

'Don't know yet.'

'You don't know?'

'Lap of the gods.'

'Really, Kate. You're as bad as Izzy.'

64

I change tack: 'How about Sam and I come visiting on Thursday?'
'Which Thursday?'
'This Thursday.'
'Can't do Thursday. Friday might be a possibility. Let me see ...
Derek!' She shouts at my father. 'Can we do Friday for Kate and
Sam?'
I hear the flick of pages. Diary? Recipe book? There's some mum-
bling and then Jean comes back on the line.
'Should be OK,' she reports.
'Sandwiched in between the buffets,' I say.
And I laugh.

On Friday I pick Sam up from school at twelve o'clock and we drive
over the Downs to Henfield. My parents' house is on the outskirts of
the village, an unengaging brick building bought for its 'useful in-
terior' and its huge garden. I would have liked Sam to be able to romp
on the grass or swing on the swing his own garden is too small for, or
just have enough room to run and to hide. But the garden has been
rotovated into a giant vegetable patch. This is Derek's terrain, a
manly, mystical place where hard slog is called 'a labour of love'. My
mother does not interfere. She keeps the herb beds nearer the house.
When we arrive Derek and Jean are in the kitchen. They are always
in the kitchen. Paul thinks they probably don't know what the rest of
their house looks like. But then there isn't really much more to the
house anyway as the kitchen has gradually expanded, knocking itself
through into the hall and the drawing-room.
'You wait,' says Paul, 'the loo will be in there next.'
The original kitchen is Jean's 'business end'. She has an Aga, a gas
stove and a gas hob as well as an American-style fridge, two dish-
washers and a walk-in larder. The pine table ('useful chopping
surface') is a twelve-seater, but Jean and Derek rarely entertain
anyone but themselves. The hall part of the room is office space and
the sagging shelves (not Derek's forte) spill with catering-sized cling-
film and silver foil, precariously balanced aluminium serving trays
and good-quality thick white paper napkins. The drawing-room now
hosts two chest freezers and numerous store cupboards. Squashed
into one corner is a sofa and a television set which I've never seen
switched on.
'Sit up,' says my mother. She positions Sam in front of a plate of
poached salmon, mayonnaise sauce with gherkins, cherry tomatoes

(I've no idea where she gets cherry tomatoes at this time of year), boiled potatoes and a buttered bagel.

'Yuk,' says Sam.

'Sam ...' I begin, warningly but without enthusiasm. Jean knows her grandson is a pasta and cheese man.

'But I don't like them,' he says, pushing his fork at the gherkins. 'And I don't like them either.' The cherry tomatoes.

'It's all that Heinz baby food you gave him,' Jean remarks.

'Well, just eat what you do like,' I tell him, 'the fish and the cream sauce.'

'What fish?'

'The pink fish.'

'I like grey fish, Gran.'

Gran smiles. Sam's faults are mainly laid at my door which is something to be thankful for, I suppose. In her own way, Jean likes her only grandchild. The fact that she allows him to call her Gran is proof of that. One day, when I'm feeling bold, I shall ask her why she can be Gran but not Mum.

I eat my poached salmon. Sam eats his bagel. Derek has a sandwich and Jean has nothing. For a cook, she is a twig of a woman.

'Why aren't you eating any lunch, Gran?'

'Too busy.'

Sam pushes his plate away.

'Finish up,' says Gran.

'Too busy,' says Sam.

Gran laughs and gets him trifle.

After lunch Derek, who has said nothing since we arrived, puts on his boots.

'Where you going, Grandad?'

'Double dig the new potatoes.'

'Me too!' shouts Sam and the boys go off together. Later I shall sneak a look at them out of the window. My father and my son will be digging together strenuously, absorbedly and in silence; chatter-box Sam content in this bond. It's a sight I find strangely moving.

'I've thought about the weekend,' says Jean, 'and I don't think it's on.'

'But you don't even know which weekend it is!'

'We're very busy just now.' She is bringing to the table an array of spices in large jars.

'This holiday's very important to me, Jean.'

'Take Sam then. Take Tessa.' She measures six tablespoons of turmeric into a mixing bowl. Then six of cinnamon, six of cumin.

'It's not that sort of holiday.'

'Oh?' She pours coriander seeds into a mortar and starts to grind.

'It's a baby-making break.'

'Oh, I see.' She begins to chop chillies. 'Still no luck then?'

If she wasn't my mother I'd ram the chillies down her throat. I might ram them down anyway. Does she think I wouldn't have told her?

'No luck,' I inform her.

'Well, Sam isn't three yet,' she says.

'He's three and a half.'

'Too close an age gap is nothing but trouble.' She adds fenugreek, dry mustard and ginger.

'I wanted the gap to be two years. If I conceived tomorrow it would be over four.' This thought obsesses me. 'I don't want them growing up like two strangers. Two only children.' The word 'two' is difficult for me to say.

'Well, the fourteen years between you and Izzy didn't seem to make a lot of difference.' Black pepper and garlic salt.

I know this fact should comfort me but it doesn't. I think of my relationship with Izzy as special, defying the odds.

'I can't wait fourteen years,' I tell her. 'I'll be forty-six.'

'You never could wait,' she says, 'even as a baby.'

'Did you like me,' I ask, 'when I was a baby?'

'What an extraordinary question!'

'Did you?' I press her.

She pauses, poppy seeds in the air.

'I'm not sure it's a question of "liking".'

'I'd kill for Sam,' I say. 'I'd die for him.'

'Oh, but he's a boy!' She releases the poppy seeds.

'What!'

'Boys are different. Mothers feel differently about sons.' She crushes cardamom.

'You'd have loved me more if I'd been a boy?'

She pours the mixed spices into a large Kilner jar.

'I don't think I can answer that.'

'Do you love me now?' The question is screaming round the kitchen.

I watch her shake, add a dash of vinegar and seal the jar.

'Curry powder,' she says.

Sam and his muddy boots come into the kitchen.

'Mum,' he says, 'I love you, but . . .'

'But what?'

'But I'd like a biscuit.'

Gran gets him a biscuit and he pads away again.

As I watch him go I think, when do the 'buts' start getting bigger?

10

On Saturday the travel agent rings.

'Mrs Francis?'

Usually I'm very strict about 'Ms', but not today.

'Yes,' I say, 'yes?'

'It's Madrid,' he says. 'Thursday 10th October through Sunday 13th. Three star hotel, Carlos V.'

'Oh. Terrific. Thanks.' I pause. 'Was Prague all booked?'

'I didn't try Prague,' he says.

'Did you try anywhere else?'

'No. Just Madrid. First time lucky.'

'Oh sure. Madrid's marvellous. Terrific. Thanks. Send me the bill!'

'I already have,' he assures me.

I put down the phone as Paul and Sam come back into the house. They've been up to the electrical shop to buy light bulbs.

'Look!' says Sam. 'Look!' He's waving an ice-cream, the sort with a thick wodge of chocolate in the middle.

'Your Dad . . .' I say.

Sam laughs and disappears into the playroom.

'. . . is soft.' I conclude.

Paul shrugs. 'Saturday,' he says.

I take Paul's hand, lead him into the kitchen.

'Do you know where you're going in a few Saturdays' time?'

'Where?'

'Madrid.'

'Madrid!'

'Yes, Madrid.'

'Why the hell am I going to Madrid!'

'See the Prado?' I offer.

'The Prado!'

'Get some exercise.'

'What?'

'You said book something. Book anything, you said.'

'Rome! We agreed Rome next.'

'You wanted Rome. I wanted Prague.'

'So you booked Madrid.'

'The agent booked Madrid.'

'Well, you must have asked him to!'

'I gave him the option.'

'You gave him the option. Have you gone mad, Kate?'

'Ease up, you said. Go with the flow.'

'Rubbish. That's Izzy talk. And unlike your dear sister, I generally retain some basic common sense.'

'Do you want me to try and change it?'

He laughs suddenly. 'No, of course not. And actually I'd love to see the Prado. And *Guernica*. They do have *Guernica*, don't they? And we really haven't touched Spain before. It'll be an adventure.'

From another man I would suspect irony, but not from Paul. In the twist of one sentence he has capitulated, accommodated. He will not give the matter another thought. He is content.

I could smash the light bulbs over his head. I still want to go to Prague.

The door bell rings.

It's a lumpy little parcel from Izzy.

'Can I open it?' asks Sam, appearing from nowhere.

He pulls at the sellotape, rips the brown paper. On to the floor drops a bag of what look like small dry bones.

'What is it?' says Sam, intrigued.

I pick up the bones and undo the knotted plastic bag. Inside is a second plastic bag stamped with the insignia of the Loon Fung Supermarket. The bones are the product of The People's Republic of China. They are, according to the English translation of the Chinese characters, pieces of Angelica Root.

'Pooh-ee!' says Sam, putting a knarled specimen to his nose. 'Pooh-ee yuk stinkbomb!'

'Chuck 'em,' says Paul.

The roots smell dusty, Chinesey, faintly dangerous. I try to break one, it resists. I try a second, thinner one. It snaps. Inside, the root is slightly moister and smells, at least, living.

I unfold Izzy's missive, a scrawl on yellow paper. It is headed 'Tung Kwai'.

1. Heat root under grill till soft enough to cut. Cut 3–4 slices.

2. Put slices in slow cooker with whole chicken. (Remove skin to lessen fat or leave liquid to cool afterwards and remove fat.) Add a little water.
3. Leave on low power overnight or for 12 hours.
4. Drink the fluid. (You can eat the chicken if you want.)
5. Ginseng based.
6. Use once a week but *not* the week before your period is due.

If your lips are dry you are too yang (hot) so stop using. It should warm you up – you're probably too ying (cool) hence your cold feet.

After that there is some love-you-forever stuff and then a bracket: '(Tin chat for men.)'

'What is it, Mum?' Sam repeats.

'It's a voodoo fertility rite from your Aunt Izzy.'

'Voodotility!' he chants. 'Voodotility!'

'I thought your sister believed in a Christian God,' Paul remarks.

'We don't have a slow cooker. I wonder if it would work as well in an ordinary oven?'

Paul leans over my shoulder and reads the recipe.

'Over my dead body am I eating that!'

'It's not for you, it's for me. You get Tin Chat.'

'Tin chat? Tin chat!'

He stalks into the hall with a ladder and the light bulbs.

'Tin chat is all I get from your family!'

Sam spirits three pieces of root away into the playroom. I don't pursue him. There are about fourteen left and, at three slices a week, each one looks as though it would last a month at least. Another person sending me more than a year's supply of fertility drugs would not earn my thanks. With Izzy, as ever, it's different. I'm touched by the thought of her carrying my burden into a Chinese supermarket. And she must have done some research. The uses of Angelica Root are not noted on the packet. She must have inquired, found out, cared. And there have been times when I've thought, because she's so young, because a child is so far from her own imaginings, that she couldn't know, didn't care. I tip the bones back into the bag and tie the knot. Then I go to the calendar to mark in the Madrid dates.

'Aargh!'

Sam runs from the playroom. Paul clatters from the ladder.

'What the hell...'

'The Madrid weekend! It's when my period's due!'

'For heaven's sake.' Paul's relief is audible.

'See what happens when I leave things to chance! To fate!'

'Oh, Kate!' Paul has begun to laugh. 'It'll take the strain off us, anyhow!'

'Oh, great. Terrific.'

Paul comes towards me, puts his arms round me, laughs into my neck. 'Oh, Kate, Kate.'

Sam, sensing that everything will be all right, drifts away.

Paul's kissing me now, and I feel the tips of his fingers behind my ears. He kisses my throat and then his hands travel down the back of my neck, the length of my spine and on to, over my buttocks.

'Anyway,' he says, 'you may not get your next period.'

'If his Gran don't want him,' says Tessa, chewing through a white bacon roll (Monday breakfast), 'I'll have him. When you go to Italy.'

'Spain.'

'What?' Her mouth is ringed with white bap flour.

'Madrid's in Spain.'

'Oh. You never been to Spain, have you?'

'No.'

'It's great. You'll love it.'

Last time she went to Spain, Tessa came back with tales of how she was the only girl to take part in the Endurance Test.

'There was five of us. You stood on a crate and they poured this stuff on you.'

'What stuff?'

'Everyfing. Tomato sauce. Baked beans. Flour. And raw eggs. You had to eat those. They put them in your mouth. The one who stood longest, they won. I won. I got a bottle of champagne.' She showed me a picture, Tessa in her bean-bloodied swimming costume, smiling a huge smile and waving a very cheap bottle of Spanish fizzy.

'Cost you a new costume, didn't it?' I ventured.

'Don't be stupid. Kevin licked it all off!' She burst into hysterical laughter. 'Only kidding you. You're not shocked? You are, aren't you!'

'Mortified and astounded.'

'What?'

'And appalled. I thought you said there was no romance.'

'What?'

'Kevin.'

72

'Oh, Kevin! He was just a mate. You would think that, wouldn't you!'

'Think what?'

'You know.' Tessa nods.

I don't know. The workings of Tessa's mind are always wondrous to me.

'So what do you think,' she asks me now, crushing the bacon bap bag, 'about me having him?'

'I'm hoping his Gran's going to change her mind.' I get up, collect my keys, my purse, my wallet, my things for the office.

'You don't trust me, do you?'

'It's not that.'

'It is! You don't trust me. I done it loads of times before. I looked after one little girl for two weeks when her parents went away.'

'It's not you,' I tell her, 'it's me. You know how obsessive I am about him. I'd just worry. It's because of me, not you.'

Tessa gets up and throws the greasy bag in the bin.

'We'd have a great time, Sam and me. We'd have a ball.'

Sam pads into the kitchen.

'Wouldn't we, Sam?'

'What?' says my son.

Later that week, when Sam is at school, I visit Steven Seligman, Dip. Phyt. MNIMH. Seligman belongs to the Maple Down Clinic of Natural Medicine. Or maybe the clinic belongs to him. I'm dubious about the place, but not as dubious as Paul.

'A what clinic?'

'A clinic of Natural Medicine.' I spotted it, quite by chance, as I walked alone on Sunday afternoon. 'Seligman's a Medical Herbalist.'

'A quack, you mean.'

'Possibly.'

'Well, if it makes you feel better to pay to see a quack, why not?'

'Who's to say that Baboneau's not a quack?' I counter.

'Who indeed,' says Paul, 'though at least he's a conventional quack.'

'Ducks go quack,' says Sam.

What have I got to lose? I can visit the quack or use the money to buy a slow cooker to boil a bunch of Chinese bones.

I ring the clinic.

'What exactly is Natural Medicine?' I ask. I have decided that if the

73

receptionist smirks down the phone, I won't book. She does not smirk. She explains in a voice which is mesmeric with concern.

'If you would like to meet Mr Seligman,' she finishes, 'before making a decision about booking, then he's available for pre-consultation chats between 2 and 3 p.m. on Wednesdays. No appointment necessary and no fee of course.'

I am persuaded.

'I'll book the real thing,' I say.

And so, at 9.45 on Thursday morning I arrive at the clinic. It's a large, gracious building with a curved flight of steps to its solid, natural wood door. 'Please ring and enter,' says a brass plaque. So I do.

Inside it looks, and smells, rather like a beauty clinic – the décor fresh white, grass green, the doors glass and the aroma of mint and of tea. The receptionist sits at a white desk in a white coat. Her appointments book is bound white leather, her rubber plant waxy green and her lamp brass with a green glass shade. Her face is oval, white, high priestess. She wears her straight black hair in a pony tail to her waist. I think her fabulously beautiful.

I introduce myself.

'Of course,' she says, 'Ms Francis,' and she gives me the sort of smile which feels like a caress. 'Do take a seat. Steven will be with you in just one moment.'

She points to a waiting-room of plants and green chairs and a polished table laid with leaflets on healthy minds and bodies. I see that in this clinic you may have acupuncture, stress management, Qi Gong, chiropody, aromatherapy, massage therapy, reflexology, a podiatrist (a podiatrist?) to visit your home, a doctor called Help to jump on your back. One leaflet particularly attracts my attention, 'Yin Yang'. 'The balance of opposites,' I read, 'complementary to one another in all living things, which creates a perfect living whole. Yin Yang symbolizes man and woman, land and sea, earth and sky, east and west, nature and science, acid and alkaline.' The leaflet is for beauty products.

'Ms Francis?' A face beams in. 'I'm Steven Seligman. I'm so sorry to keep you.'

He hasn't kept me. He too has a tactile smile. He's a relaxed man, slightly sunburnt, with the top button of his shirt undone as if he'd just that moment returned from a yachting holiday which, had he known you the moment before, he would undoubtedly have invited you to accompany him on.

'Do come this way.'

74

I follow his embracing arms into a large comfortable, comforting room. There are books and papers and of course a desk. But there are also water-colours of geraniums in Italy and men playing boules in France. There are photographs of his own children, two boys, and fresh flowers picked from the garden which runs, a riot of colour still, beyond the french windows. He sits in front of, not behind the desk and my chair is the exact twin of his.

'Tell me why you've come,' he says.

And I tell him as though it's a dream, telling him things I've hardly told myself, let alone Mr James Baboneau. He nods and smiles and I know that he thinks it is all relevant: my relationship with my mother, my passion for Izzy, my terror that Sam will die.

He murmurs, he says, 'Oh yes' and 'Of course' as if all my madness is sane.

'And your husband?' he inquires softly.

'Is fine,' I say, 'has four times the sperm of an average man and is utterly unphased by non-conception. He thinks it'll happen. If not now, then later.'

'Ah,' says call-me-Steven Seligman. 'Which doesn't make it any easier for you, of course.'

'Of course,' I say and the balm runs hot down my back.

'What would your husband say if you asked him to keep the three or four days round ovulation special? To make them private, where you took special time for yourselves, deliberately chose not to go out visiting, but planned to do things just the two of you, together?'

I laugh. 'He'd think it was sex therapy.'

'And do you think it's sex therapy?'

'No. Personally,' (I'm doing very well here, I haven't cried yet) 'I'd welcome anything that involved him, gave him a role, an obligation.'

'You feel very much alone in this, don't you?'

'Yes! Yes.'

'But how can you not be in this together? The body is not divisible from the mind. It matters how you feel...'

(It matters how I feel!)

'... and it matters how he feels. How you are together. Sharing, understanding, staying relaxed or trying to stay relaxed. Think about holiday pregnancies, they are a fact medical science just can't explain.'

'I want to regain control,' I tell him suddenly. 'I feel like I've surrendered myself to medical science. There are months, you know, when I think just taking the drugs will make me pregnant, when I'm astonished that my period comes when I've faithfully, religiously taken the pills. One a day. Two a day. And then I think if I didn't take

75

the pills, just trusted to my body, that I'd never become pregnant. I've lost faith in my body, lost faith with myself.'

'You must regain that faith,' says Steven. 'Your body works. Think of your son.'

'Worked,' I say, 'past tense.'

'No,' says Steven. 'Works. Present tense.'

'How can I know that? How can I be sure?'

'There are no absolutes,' says Steven. 'But there don't have to be. Believe it and it will be true. That's all that matters.'

'It's no better than religion,' I say, thinking of Izzy.

'And no worse,' says Steven.

'And medical science?'

'Everything has its place,' says Steven. 'But think of the facts. You have put your faith in conventional medicine and, to date, your god has played you false. What have you to lose?'

'Why have I put my faith in medical science?' I wonder suddenly.

'Because science has faith in itself. It believes it has the answers so strongly, that you have been persuaded. Besides, your acclimatization has been long. You know a doctor can bandage your knee, so you think he can deliver you a baby. But a baby and a bandaged knee are not one and the same.'

'Can you deliver me a baby?'

'No. Of course not. But you can deliver yourself a baby. You and your husband together. That I believe with all my heart.'

Now I do begin to cry.

'And in as far as I can help you,' says Steven, 'I will.'

After that we talk about my work, my lifestyle, my diet. I tell him proudly how good my diet is, how full of polyunsaturates, of oily fish, of bran. He thinks maybe I eat too much bran.

'Have you tried muesli,' he says, 'with apple juice?'

I tell him how, approximately ten days before my period, I have a craving for chocolate. He says maybe I have a potassium shortage, I should treat myself to some Brazil nuts.

Then, finally, he takes out a piece of paper and begins to murmur spells, his blue ink flowing in hieroglyphs across the page.

'What are you prescribing?' I ask.

'A moment,' he says, for his concentration must not be broken.

I wait. My mother would be proud.

'Three medicines,' he says at last. 'Each for different parts of the month, to fit in with your own natural cycle. To accentuate or balance only those things your own body knows best. And some tea. A very

76

good herb tea which you can use at your own discretion, when you feel in need of relaxation.'

Then it is time to go. I have been in his surgery, his room, for an hour and a half and it has cost me less than half what it costs to see Baboneau for quarter of an hour. What's more I feel different — positive. I feel like a human being.

'If you need to call me at any time,' says Steven, 'then call. I'm always available except when I'm with a patient. And then I'll call you straight back. OK?'

'OK,' I say, 'and thank you.'

He shakes my hand.

I give the prescription to the High Priestess. She arises from her green chair, Venus from the shell.

'Would you like to wait?' she asks, 'or collect later?'

'I'll wait,' I say.

She smiles. 'I'll do it for you now, then.'

She puts on black, oval-rimmed glasses and she drifts towards a white door. Behind the door are shelves and shelves of dark glass jars, white-stoppered, glass-stoppered. I am mad to go in and watch. I creep and sidle.

'Do you mind?' I ask her, arriving against the door.

'Not at all,' she says.

The room is small and the High Priestess (who must surely only be the receptionist today by default) works at a white marble slab. She looks at the hieroglyphs and then at the bottles, the tinctures and fluid extracts. They are arranged alphabetically, each one labelled in white, handwritten, each one part of a greater whole, a greater spell: Anemone Pulsatilla; Juniperus Communis; Passiflora Incarnata (oh Passiflora Incarnata!) and the slinking Lycopus Virg.

She begins. She washes her hands. She lifts the tiny glass measures with their white glass lips. She selects and pours: Salvia, Humulus, Zingiber Officinale.

'What are they?' I ask.

'Sage,' she says, 'hops, ginger and this, Matricaria, is camomile, or beloved mother. Caria — beloved. Matria — mother, the matrix, the network of all life.'

Oh, Alleluiah! responds my heart.

She touches and lifts the Viburnum Prunifolium, sub-labelled Black Haw, and with it the Viburnum Opulus.

'Cramp bark,' she says. 'And this is Valeriana Officinalis: "to be well". He's very good, Steven. Have you been before?'

'No,' I say.

She smiles.

'What's your name?' I ask.

'Diana,' she says.

'The huntress.' I say. 'Goddess of the Moon.' What else.

'White deadnettle,' she replies, 'Lamium Albium and also Leonurus, that's motherwort.' She adds one drop of Oil of Fennel and the scent fills the room. Then a touch of Vitex Agnes Castus. 'The Chaste Tree. They gave it to monks, to suppress the desire. But in women . . .' Diana, the Huntress smiles her chaste smile. Her teeth are very white.

The larger bottle she then fills to the rim with Chamaelirium Luteum: False Unicorn Root. To the second she adds Hypericum.

'St John's wort,' she tells me, 'fresh and organic. Steven makes it himself.' From behind a brown bottle of Eyebright Euphrasia she draws a transparent cork-stoppered bottle three-quarters full of what looks like blood and oil.

'See,' she says, 'here are the flowers.' Sunk beneath the blood is a dense brown swirl of vegetable matter. 'He's very good, you know.' And I do know – know where her chaste love lies.

When the three bottles are full, she screws on white caps and labels them carefully. One to be taken every day, one to stop at Day 9, one to begin on Day 11. Medicines A, B and C, marked in black felt-tip. I feel they should be marked in blood.

'And now the tea.' She lifts down Chinese tins. 'Melissa,' she says, 'or lemon balm. And Turnera, Damiana.'

'What does Damiana mean?'

'Just the name of the botanist who discovered the plant.'

But just as I cannot think of Hypericum without thinking of Hamlet, I cannot think of Damiana, without thinking of the Devil.

She puts the medicine bottles in white chemists' bags and the tea in a thick white coffee-bean bag. She hands them to me with a smallish bill.

'I have a question.'

'Ask,' she says.

'Can I take the herbs alongside the conventional drugs,' I say, 'or not?'

Her eyes darken to violet.

'You must ask that of Steven.'

She calls him and I repeat my question, feeling like a charlatan.

'The herbs are very powerful,' Steven says. 'They and your body together. They may override the conventional drugs. Ideally it would be better just to use the herbs. But this must be your choice. There is certainly no danger to you in taking both.'

I feel good about it being my choice. I thank him and his High Priestess and I leave.

I know that I shall take both drugs and herbs. Just as I know that, in doing so, I will not be so much regaining control of my life, as hedging my bets.

11

I'm not supposed to start the herbs until Day 1 of my next cycle. But I start them anyway. I also start the tea.

'Make as for ordinary tea. Leave to stand for five minutes. Strain. *Sip.* No milk. No sugar.'

I strain. But the tea still floats with little twigs and it smells like a swimming pool. This makes it preferable to the medicines, especially the one with the St John's wort which is so evil it makes me want to retch. In the noxious fumes I scent Damiana, the Devil, he breathes on my neck. Maybe I would have been better off with the bones after all.

Izzy rings.

'How are you?' she says.

'Fumigating,' I tell her.

'Did you try the Angelica Root?'

'Not yet,' I say. 'We don't have a slow cooker. But I will,' I add, changing the subject, 'when we get back from Madrid.'

'You're going to Madrid?'

'Spontaneous decision.'

'Oh wow!'

'And Jean's looking after Sam.' This is the good news on the Madrid dates. Much to Tessa's chagrin, it's the one weekend my mother is free. *Of course Derek and I will look after him. He'll be no trouble. It's only you who make such heavy weather out of him.* 'She's over the moon.'

'Tell me another.'

'Another,' I tell her. 'And by the way, how's the job search going?'

'Fine.'

'Any interviews?'

'Something will turn up.'

'It's nearly October,' I inform her.

'October', says my sister, 'is a lifetime of opportunities away.'

Three short weeks pass and then it is 9 October. Jean and Derek have decided to look after Sam in the familiarity of his own home.

'Thanks,' I say, 'I'm sure it'll be much easier for him, being here.'

My father nods. 'Your mother wants to see the new kitchen equipment place anyway. Dukes Lane. Opens tomorrow.'

'Why kill one bird', says Jean, 'when you can kill two?'

That's what they say on Wednesday night. I put Sam to bed and kiss him as though I shall never see him again. I have briefed him well. He knows we are going to Madrid. He knows he is staying home with his grandparents. He has observed our suitcases. Thus far he has reserved judgement. But all too soon it is Thursday morning and we are departing.

Sam is sitting in the playroom watching his breakfast video. It's Captain Planet. I have rushed my last-minute tasks, have abandoned them, to secure this special segment of time with my son. I sit beside him on the sofa, take his hand.

'In a minute,' I say, 'Daddy and I have to go.'

'Captain Planet', says Sam, 'is a hero.' Without taking his eyes from the screen, he withdraws his hand from mine, takes his cup of milk and drinks.

Paul puts his head round the door.

'I've ordered the taxi,' he says.

'Why!'

'Well, you're ready aren't you? I thought you said you were ready.'

'But we've got hours!'

Paul comes into the room and kisses Sam's head.

'Bye, Sam.'

'Bye, Dad.'

Paul leaves.

'Sam,' I say urgently, 'we're going to Madrid. Granny and Grampi are going to look after you. And Tessa. I'll phone you every night and be back very soon. I love you, Sam. Give us a hug.'

I'm aware of a thin presence at the door.

'I'd go', says Jean, 'while the going's good.'

But I don't want the going to be good. I want it to be hard.

'Sam,' I say, 'Sam . . .' But my loving, hugging child is staring at the box.

'Taxi's here,' shouts Paul.

'Come and see us off, Sam. Come and wave the taxi off.'

'No,' says Sam.

'We must save the Earth,' says Captain Planet. 'Nothing is more important than that!'

81

'Come on,' says Paul, 'come on!'

I take Sam in my arms, I kiss him. He struggles to see the screen.

'Goodbye,' I say, 'I love you.'

Nothing.

'Say goodbye, Sam.'

'Bye,' he says.

Then I have to walk out the door and climb into the taxi.

Waving us off are Jean and Derek. Before we turn the corner, Jean has closed our front door.

'Wonderful,' says Paul. 'Freedom at last!'

We arrive in Madrid in the early afternoon. The glass doors of the airport slide back and we step into the hot dry heat of Spain. And there it is – even among the fumes and the tarmac – that smell which always makes my heart leap; the smell of dust and of rot and of flowers which, with the suddenness of the heat and the shimmer of the air, says, 'Come, touch, taste, this land awaits you.' I never feel this about cold countries.

'Shall we take a taxi?' Paul asks.

But I want to take the coach. It's cheaper and it makes me feel more indigenous. I also have an Anglo-Saxon horror of being cheated. The coach has dark glass windows, cool air-conditioning and a hot babble of Spanish. I watch and listen as we roar and traffic-jam into the city centre. The coach puts us down in an underground car-park in the Plaza de Colon, next to a line of taxis.

'I am not taking the metro,' says Paul, and he waves at a taxi man.

'Hotel Carlos,' I begin, and then realize I do not know how to say 'V', so I say it in English, 'Fifth.' Then I add, 'Maestro Vitoria Street. Via Maestro Vitoria?'

The taxi man gives a quick nod and throws our bags in the boot.

I try to follow our transit on the map. We head in the right direction but then detour, or I think we detour, I can't follow the one-way systems.

The taxi stops and the driver, who seems to be permanently on fast-forward, snaps off the meter, leaps out, and nods furiously at a building labelled Hotel Castilla La Nueva. Paul opens his door.

'It's the wrong hotel,' I say.

'What!'

I point at the map the travel agent has given us, where the name of the hotel is written in biro.

'No,' I say to the taxi driver, 'Hotel Carlos Fifth.'

He looks at the map, throws up his hands, shouts, laughs and then waves at the Castilla's doorman. He jumps in again and streams Spanish at us. I look at the blank meter. He can now charge us what he likes.

Five minutes later we are at the right hotel. It's located on a pedestrianized street which the driver declines to turn up, leaving us to drag our suitcases to the door ourselves. Paul pays him what he asks (more than the entire fare from the airport as noted in my guidebook) and tips him generously.

Then he looks at my face.

'Don't fuss,' he says.

'He had us! The bastard!'

'You should have showed him the map in the first place.'

'You didn't have to tip him that much.'

'I didn't have any change.'

I pull at my suitcase. Paul stills my hand.

'Kate,' he says, 'please . . .'

'Please what?'

'Please relax. It doesn't matter.'

And of course it doesn't, which makes me angrier still.

In the cool of the hotel foyer I calm down. The receptionist smiles. He speaks English. He has a note of our reservation.

'Fourth floor,' he says.

A lackey comes with us in the tiny lift. He carries our cases, or rather struggles with them until Paul helps him out, to Room 414. He smiles as he puts the key in the lock, as he gestures us in. I see Paul reaching for his wallet at the same time as I see the beds.

'Twins!' I scream. 'They've put us in twins!'

'Eh?' inquires the lackey.

'We asked for a double bed. We booked a double.' I leer at him. 'Confirmed it.'

'Doesn't matter,' says Paul. 'We can push them together.'

'Eh?' repeats the lackey.

'It bloody well does matter.' I ring the receptionist.

'No,' he says, 'I don't have any double bed booking for you. No. No, I don't.'

Does he apologize? Does he offer to change our room?

'We are full tonight,' he says. 'Maybe, tomorrow, perhaps? Maybe we may do something tomorrow?'

'Or even the day after,' I say, 'or the day after that, when we're about to leave.'

'Pardon?' he says.

'*Mañana*,' says Paul.

'Eh,' says the lackey and disappears with Paul's money.

I sit down on the edge of one of the twins. Paul goes to the window and opens the shutters. Sunlight streams into the olive green room. He opens the windows. We have a small, iron-balustraded balcony. Sounds of the street lift from the pavement below.

'Come on.' Paul takes my hand and pulls me into the light. 'Look.' The siesta is over. The shops are opening again. Brightly coloured men and women go about their business. In our little street there is a leather goods shop, a smart ladies' wear shop, a jeweller. Further away a street trader begins to lay out his wares, beads, purses, silver. Two young women walk arm in arm, chatting.

'It's our holiday,' Paul says. 'They'll be a *mercato*.'

I find my arm going round his waist.

'OK?' he says.

'OK,' I say.

And we kiss.

A change of sandals later we are out on the streets. In England we never hold hands any more. But in the Calle Maestro Vitoria his hand finds mine. We follow the map to the Puerto del Sol. But we are not going there, or indeed anywhere at all. We are just walking. There is a sudden lightness to Paul's step, almost a gaiety. I notice this, I realize with a sense of shock, because it is so unusual. As he pauses to inspect a gentlemen's outfitters, I look at his face. It seems to me that I haven't looked at his face for a very long time. The curve of his mouth is still unbearably beautiful and his eyes softer than I remember, greyer. He turns self-consciously, aware of my gaze. And then I see something else, I see that he has suffered too, carried his own silent burden, and I want to speak about it but I can't. I, who can always talk, can say nothing to this man I love, to tell him I know, all of a sudden, that he, in his own way, suffers.

'Shoes are expensive,' he says.

And I say, 'Yes.'

We walk on. I would squeeze his hand but he has taken his hand away to point out a street name hand-painted on tiles, embedded into the side of a house. A street which must mean wolves because the tiles howl with them.

'Isn't it strange,' he says, a few minutes later as he stops to decode a menu, 'not having Sam?'

And I say, 'Yes.'

We are simultaneously moving much more slowly and much faster than usual. We cross roads at random, clinging to kerbs because of traffic, not fear. We take detours which don't feel like detours because they add no fatigue. We pause to look at clothes, at ceramics, at architecture, we neither dawdle nor hurry. We are moving at a pace we have forgotten. Our own pace. Yet Sam walks with us still, for we stop at toy-shops and feel sentimental about guns, we move slowly past parks and remark on the flavour of *gelati* he would have liked.

Eventually we arrive at the Palacio Real and we buy tickets because there is no reason not to. Paul also buys a guidebook and informs me that this neo-classical palace was completed in 1764 at which time Charles III took up residence. He reads on as we go into the Armeria Real. Here are a hundred suits of armour, knights mounted on horseback with visors down and helmets plumed. Here are crossbows, lances, shields, swords, rifles and wheel-lock pistols.

Paul looks up from his book.

'He'd have loved this.'

And we laugh because though we have learned to work without Sam we do not know how to take our leisure without him.

An hour later we have done the Throne Room, the Royal Chapel, the painting galleries, the Sala de Porcelana, and the astonishing Salon de Gasparini with its high relief of fruits and vines which leap from walls and twist from ceilings.

'And it's not even 6.15,' says Paul.

We lope into a café in the adjoining Plaza de Oriente. Paul chooses a shaded table and orders black coffee without looking at the menu. I study everything on offer. The 'words and phrases' section of my American Express guide leaves more than a third of the silver words untranslated. When the waiter returns I point to something on the white card.

'What are you having?' asks Paul.

'I don't know,' I say.

What arrives is a swirl of translucent liquid in a sun-rainbowed glass. There is also a small jug of water.

'Is it Pernod?'

I smell it.

'Cantaloups.'

'What?'

'I think it's a melon liqueur.' I sip and the liquid is sweet and fiery and, in the heat, heady.

'Is it good?'

'Delicious.'

Paul takes a small pack of cigars from his pocket and lights up. And there we sit in the sun, two grown-ups together, drinking, smoking, not needing to say anything.

We have a second round of drinks. This time Paul has beer and I have an apricot concoction. We pay no attention to the time and yet we contrive to arrive back in our hotel at precisely 7.30 p.m., 6.30 p.m. British time. The time we said we'd call Sam.

'Hello, Jean, it's me.'

'Oh, hello, how is it?'

'Terrific. Hot. How's Sam?'

'Fine. He's fine. Do you want a word?'

'Please.'

Sam comes on the line.

'Hello, Mum,' he says, 'I love you. Bye.'

'Hang on,' I say, 'hang on . . .'

Paul takes the phone from me.

'Sam?'

'Afraid he's gone.' I hear Jean's voice. 'Making soup with his grandpa.'

Paul looks disappointed but he still says, 'Thanks, Jean. Don't keep him up too late. We'll call tomorrow.'

After this we shower. Paul goes into the white bathroom first and I hear the spurt and hiss of water. He emerges some ten minutes later looking scrubbed, a white towel round his waist and his hair tousled.

'It's great,' he says, 'really hard.' He grins.

I strip off, climb into the bath and pull the shower screens round me. I open the tiny bar of hotel soap. Paul of course has used his own, brought from England. The hotel soap is white and bland but I like it anyway. I soap and slither under the running water. I wash my hair not because it needs washing but because I have the time and want the water to keep on flowing, want to move in time with it. I feel fresh, alive.

When I come back into the bedroom, Paul is lying naked on the olive green counterpane. He's reading, one hand holding the Palacio Real guidebook, the other toying with his cock. As he hears me he puts down the book. I go to lie beside him. He turns to me and smiles. It's the smile of his particular sex, not lascivious, just knowing. The set of his mouth is just as it was that first time he ever kissed me. He knows we will fuck just as I know it. And for the first time in twenty months I don't think, 'What's the point, it's far too late in my cycle to conceive' because this fuck is not about that, it's about all the times we've ever fucked: about the night we slept under the stars on a mountain terrace in Greece and had our breakfast of sun-warmed peaches brought to us

86

by a toothless Greek peasant woman; about the freezing night in Innsbruck when we tore the tiger skin rug from the bed and rolled on the floor in its fur; about the seedy hotel in Paris where the drapes were red damask and there was a mirror screwed to the ceiling; and about the staircase in my parents' house that weekend they were away, a staircase they think just joins the first and second floors of their house.

Paul begins to unwrap me, his hands large and slow and, as I move closer to him, I know it will be a long time before the strokes reach my cunt.

We shower again before we leave for dinner.

'This could be dangerously cyclical,' says Paul.

Then we dress in our smart clothes and turn out on to the dusky streets where the Madrileños mill. We walk amiably, our bodies, beneath our clothes, plumply soft. We are going, linked-arms, unhurried, towards the heart of old Madrid, the Plaza Mayor. It is well past 9 p.m. now and this enclosed colonnaded square is lit with café candles. We browse, deciding between wickerwork or white iron chairs, plastic or clothed tables, tapas bars and toothpicks or starched-white waiter restaurants.

Eventually we choose a small place on the south-eastern corner; red and white chequered cloths, local wines, paella. Paul orders a large carafe or red wine, the colour of rubies.

We drink.

'Are you happy?' he asks.

'Yes.'

And I am. Not least because it's Day 27 and there isn't a single sign of blood.

The following morning, over breakfast of hot strong coffee and sweet Spanish pastries, we decide on the Prado. Though it is the other side of town, we will walk. This is one of the beauties of a small city. And Madrid is beginning to feel beautiful to me.

We return to our room and as Paul collects his change and his maps, I open the windows, the shutters. As if in response, the street floats with the sudden sound of a flute. The tune lifts into my ears, it is Pachelbel's Canon. I look for the player. He is standing in the place of yesterday's street vendor. He moves his dusky head in time with the music, lilts with the haunting melody. A canon without other in-

87

struments, the tune played insistently, fervently, over and over again. I would throw him coins, a handful of coins, if they would reach his faraway hat. And he wouldn't notice, but just keep on playing as if his life and the tune were indivisible and to stop playing would be to stop living.

It is at this moment that I feel the slip between my legs. I reach down and my hand bloodies. I go into the white, white bathroom. The tune follows me and the clots come, vicious, spilling, incarnadine, making the white bowl red.

Paul comes into the bathroom to do his teeth.

'Go away.'

'Why?' he asks.

'Please.'

He goes. From the bedroom he calls, 'Are you OK?'

'I'm bleeding.'

'Oh, Kate.'

'It doesn't matter,' I say.

He hovers at the bathroom door.

'Don't,' I say. 'It doesn't matter.'

I have never had clots like this before. So big. So brutally red.

'Oh, Kate,' he says again. And I hear that tiny break in his voice.

I also hear the flute and its song of life, life leaking.

It is twenty minutes before the flow eases and I can stand, leave the bathroom.

'We'll take it easy,' says Paul. 'We'll look after you. We'll take a taxi.'

'We'll walk,' I say.

I go and stand at the open window. The flautist takes a breath and in his short silence an iridescent bubble appears at our balcony, and then another and another. The music begins again and the bubbles stream upwards, sun-hazed into the sky. And I know with absolute hollowness that the bubbles mean a child. I look down and there he is. A blond boy about Sam's age blowing oblivious bubbles through a plastic hoop. A despair so sudden and so strong sweeps through me that, but for one thing, I would throw myself from the balcony on to the flagstones below.

'I love you,' says Paul.

And that one thing is my son.

12

We arrive home on Sunday night. Our plane is delayed and I worry that Jean will have put Sam to bed. But Sam is no fool. He has negotiated to stay up.

'Mum!' he screams as we open the door, and he runs down the corridor and leaps into my arms.

For now, it is enough.

Then he greets his Dad.

'Have you got me a present?' he asks.

And of course we have. We have brought him authentic Spanish castanets with red and yellow silk tassles and some international Lego – a spaceship from El Corte Ingles, the most English of department stores. Sam gives the castanets the most cursory examination and then moves ecstatically on to the Lego. He cannot go to bed until the Lego is assembled in all its glory of green and black. But then I don't want him to go to bed.

'Must be off,' says Jean. 'Busy day tomorrow.'

'Thank you for everything,' says Paul. We give them brandy from the airport and a huge can of virgin olive oil.

'By the way,' says my father, 'Tessa didn't come to work on Friday.'

'Oh?'

'She had neuralgia,' says Jean.

'Neuralgia!' Tessa's medical complaints are many and varied but they are normally confined to the evacuational – vomiting, diarrhoea, period problems.

'A woman rang in . . .'

'Rosemary,' I say, 'the woman she lives with.'

'Frankly,' says Derek, 'I thought it a little suspicious. She was perfectly all right on Thursday afternoon.'

'I'll check it out,' I say, ushering them towards the door.

'Don't pay her,' says Jean. 'That'll sort her out.' Then she calls, 'Bye, Sam.'

'Bye, Gran,' he replies from the kitchen. 'Bye, Grampi.'

She pecks me on the cheek, a hard peck like a bird's. Derek nods and then they are gone.

'Great,' says Paul.

I help Sam with the spaceship wings and finally, when the craft can fly, we ascend to bed. I close Sam's curtains and turn on his night-light. I help him undress and look at his still pale, slim boy's body. I do his teeth, brush his thick, sun-gilded hair. Then I read to him, poems about kings and queens and soldiers and cream cakes and raindrops. When he lies down to sleep, I lie beside him for a moment.

'I want to whisper something, Mum,' he says.

I put my ear close to his mouth.

'A balloon came into the room,' he hisses, 'with a ceiling on its head.'

'What!'

He giggles and then his eyes roll closed. He stretches out a blind hand to me and I take it, kiss it.

'I love you, Mum,' he says. 'I like you.'

'I love you too,' I say. 'God bless. See you in the morning.'

'See you in the morning.'

He is asleep before I have left the room.

I go into our bedroom where Paul is unpacking.

'The nicest thing about going away,' he says, 'is coming home.'

Half an hour later Tessa rings.

'Hi.'

'Hi.'

'How did you like it? Spain?'

'Terrific.'

'Told you.'

'How was it here?'

'I never had neuralgia.'

'I didn't think you did. What did you have?'

'Can't tell you.'

'Come on, Tessa.'

'I can't.'

'Period pains?' She would certainly have been too embarrassed to tell my parents this.

'No.'

'What then?'

'Can't say.'

'Tessa...'

'I was in hospital.'

'Oh? Not serious ... Serious?' I'm egging her on.

'You know.'

I don't. Though abortion crosses my mind.

'Stomach pump. I took thirty-two paracetamol.'

'What the hell did you do that for!'

'Can't tell you.'

'Tessa, I'm getting *déjà vu*.'

'What?'

But this time she will not be drawn.

'I'm OK now,' she declares finally. 'Be OK for work tomorrow. Definitely.'

'OK,' I say, 'I'll see you.'

'Did you send me a postcard?' she asks.

I relay this conversation to Paul. He's taking his shoes out of his shoe bag and putting them back in his cupboard.

'She'll have to go,' he says.

'What?'

'We can't have a potential suicide looking after Sam.'

I don't tell him he already has a potential suicide looking after Sam. 'She was obviously all right on Thursday,' I say, 'and she's all right now. I think it was just a blip.'

'A suicide attempt is never a blip,' says Paul. 'It's the suddenly visible tip of a iceberg. And icebergs don't melt.'

'Haven't you ever felt like committing suicide?'

'Don't be ridiculous.'

'I have.'

'Maybe. But you haven't actually taken the pills, have you? That's the difference.'

He closes his empty suitcase and stores it in the top of the wardrobe. I have still to begin on my unpacking.

'I wish I knew why she'd done it.'

'Doesn't matter,' says Paul. 'She tried – that's all you need to know.'

'But the problem – whatever it is – might go away or have gone away.'

'But her personality won't. It's too much of a risk, Kate.'

'She was OK on Thursday afternoon,' I repeat. 'I really don't think she brings her personal problems to work. Keeps home and work quite separate. She can turn off. That's what she's like. Anyway, if there was some sort of long-term problem, I'd have picked something up by now, wouldn't I?'

'Being able to flip so fast makes it worse not better. What if we'd done as she asked, and let her have sole charge of Sam while we were away?'

'Then I don't think she'd have taken the pills.'

'You don't *think*? Whose side are you on here? Hers or Sam's?'

On Sam's. On the suicide's. On mine. Does he think I can book someone to look after Sam between now and tomorrow morning? And on Tessa's. Why has she done it?

'You volunteering to take the day off tomorrow?' I ask him.

'What?'

'ArtsAid Day is a month away. I have to work.'

'I have to work.'

'And that's more important to you than Sam's life?' I turn the tables on him.

'Ring Julia,' says Paul.

The following day I go to London. Of course it's a compromise and of course I worry. But I have played my cards carefully. I waited to see how Tessa was when she arrived for work. She was punctual, pink-lipped, glad to see Sam. Up-front.

'I'm not never going to do it again,' she told me. 'It was disgusting.'

Why do I believe her? Maybe because she is such a definite person, definite about committing suicide, definite about not doing so. Maybe because I recognize how the urge to despair does come – and go. Maybe because ArtsAid Day is so close and I cannot afford not to believe her.

'I'd never hurt Sam,' she says. 'Never.'

And I believe that too. Her love for Sam is quite palpable. But if she flipped?

'Julia rang,' I tell her. 'She's invited you and Sam for lunch.' Julia's house is just three streets from the school. What can go wrong in three streets? 'And William's most insistent that Sam stays to tea too. You could give him his bath there and Paul could pick you both up at 6.30?'

'OK,' says Tessa, unsuspecting.

And so, having hung my safety net, I leave for the office.

In my short absence abroad, journalists have rung, printers have missed deadlines and one of my actors, Frank Jamieson, has been killed in a car crash.

'Life', says the poet, 'is the flight of a sparrow through the Great Hall.'

What if Sam never made it to school?

'It's eleven o'clock,' says Pippa. 'Bad news travels fast. You'd know by now.'

But my hand is still on the telephone.

'Tell you what,' says Pippa, 'why don't we do a Frank Jamieson Memorial? Special ArtsAid tribute. Bit of Tennyson, some tragedy, hold out the hat. We could rake it in.'

I begin to dial. After she's taken Sam to school on Mondays, Tessa has chores: cleaning the playroom, doing Sam's washing and ironing, changing his sheets.

The phone connects, rings. One ring, two rings, shall I panic? Three rings. Click. Pause.

'Hello?'

'Tessa . . .'

'Yes?'

'It's me.'

'Oh.' Vague. Normal.

'I need a phone number,' I tell her. 'It's in my black book.'

And, by the way, is my son dead?

I hear her fumble for the book.

'Hanratty,' I say. 'Harold.'

She turns pages.

'Did Sam go off to school OK?' I ask.

'Fine,' she says. 'Henretty,' she muses.

'Han,' I say, 'ratty. It's on the left-hand page.'

'Wil, Wil, Wilton . . .'

'That's it. Wilmington Way.'

'Your writing!' she says.

Tessa is slightly dyslexic. Last year's Christmas card to Sam read, 'Lost of love'. I kept that card, put it in the box with Sam's 'special things', the home-made Easter cards, the tissue flowers for Mother's Day, the Father's Day boat.

Tessa reads me the number and I take it down, even though I know it by heart.

'Thanks,' I say and replace the receiver.

'Who rings to check if Tessa's OK?' I announce, excusing myself.

Pippa does not reply, she's busy.

Soon I'm busy too. It's 1.30 before I realize I have missed the

93

dangerous walk from school to Julia's house. But then if they hadn't arrived by 12.30, Julia would have rung. Wouldn't she? Be calm. Be sensible.

'Do you want a sandwich?' Pippa goes out foraging and returns with roast beef for herself and prawn cocktail for me.

'Right, you've got ten minutes on Madrid,' she says, spreading her horseradished napkin.

The phone rings.

'Typical!' Pippa licks a finger, lifts the receiver. As she listens her tone changes. 'Oh no,' she breathes, 'oh, no.' Then, looking at me, she adds, 'Fucking hell. Fucking, fucking hell.'

My body locks. My elbows rivet to the desk.

She puts the phone down.

'I'm going to be sick,' she says.

She moves, holding her hand over her mouth, to the door and down the stairs. I hear her throat heave but I'm still stuck to the desk. She retches and with the sound there is a sudden splintering, me cracking up, away, hurtling down the steps three at a time until I'm finally there, on the landing, through the door, beside her in the loo.

'What is it?' I shake her. 'What is it!'

'One of my artists', she sicks, 'is withdrawing his picture.'

I look at the small swirl of yellow vomit.

'That good a picture?'

'God, I hate being pregnant.' She flushes the toilet, looks at me again. 'All due respect.' She rinses her mouth.

'Shit,' I say, unavoidably.

'Sorry,' she shrugs.

We ascend the stairs together.

'I got my period in Madrid,' I tell her. 'Still got it. Think I lost most of the blood in my body.' I fill her in on the clots, their consistency, colour and size. I don't spare her.

'Maybe you miscarried?' she says, eating roast beef.

'What?'

'Well, you were a little late, weren't you?'

The thought shocks me. I have been working on the theory that the increase in blood was the effect of the herbs.

'Early miscarriage', continues Pippa, 'is extremely common.'

I look at her flat, child-filled belly.

'I'd like it to be a miscarriage,' I say. 'You can't miscarry unless you've conceived.'

'Quite,' says Pippa.

The phone rings again. Again Pippa takes it.

94

'It's Julia,' she says.

'Yes?' I stretch a hand into eternity. 'Yes!' I hear Julia breathe, take a long breath. Speak, Julia, speak!

'I just thought', Julia says, 'I'd let you know it's all fine. Everything's absolutely fine.'

'Oh, Christ. Thanks, Julia.'

But everything is not fine. The space of that one breath has changed me. I know now I'm going to have to give Tessa notice.

'It's not right,' says Tessa. 'If you wanted to sack me you should have done it before. Not let me have him all yesterday.'

'I'm not sacking you, Tessa. I'm giving you one month's notice. Working notice.'

'Rosemary said I never should have told you.'

'I like your honesty. You know that. I respect it in you.'

'Oh sure. Look where it's got me! She said I should never!'

'Anyway it's not about the suicide. How many times do I have to tell you?'

'You think I'd hurt Sam, don't you!'

'No, I don't.'

'Then why!'

'Because of ArtsAid. The project will be finished in a month. The main bit anyway. And we're a charity, Tessa. The lease on our office expires. We can't be sure we'll still be in business. Depends how it goes. I can't guarantee your job because I can't guarantee mine.'

'It's not right.'

'It's not as though I haven't been warning you, Tessa.' This is partially true. 'I said right at the beginning of the summer I didn't know what would happen to the project after November.'

'That was ages ago!'

'And there's another thing. Something I only just found out.'

'What?'

'Pippa's pregnant. That alone puts the project in doubt.'

Tessa eyes me from under blue-shadowed lids.

'Sure it's not you who's pregnant?'

And there she has me, knife between the ribs.

'It is! It is!'

The knife turns.

'It is. I know it!'

'Have you any idea then,' I ask her, 'why I'm bleeding like a stuck pig?'

95

On Wednesday I work from home. It costs me a fortune in long-distance phonecalls but I don't care. I am nearer to Sam. At noon Tessa is scheduled to collect Sam from school.

At 12.15 I'm already downstairs, heating beans, grilling toast. They arrive, as normal, at 12.20 precisely. Tessa sits down at the kitchen table and opens a huge paper bag. White bap roll with egg mayonnaise. For some reason she always declines to eat with us.

'You haven't forgotten', I say, flipping the toast, 'that it's half-term next week?'

'You're kidding.'

'You had forgotten.' During school holidays Tessa's two half-days (Tuesdays and Wednesdays) turn into long days. 'But then you love being here at 8.30 a.m.'

'I was going to go down the Job Centre.' She opens another white bag. Jam doughnut. She rubs her fingers over the sugar. 'Sam'll have to come too.'

'I'd rather he didn't.'

'Why?'

'I don't think he'd find it that thrilling.'

'Are you saying I can't go?'

'Go on Thursday, go Friday.' Her days off. I butter the toast.

'The best jobs are always Wednesdays. Can I have holiday?'

'Sorry, Tessa, I have to go to London next Wednesday.'

'You owe me holiday.' She bites into the egg mayonnaise. 'I can take it when I want.'

'We agreed I'd pay you the holiday instead. You know I can't take the time off just now.'

'You just went to Spain.'

'Thursday through Sunday.'

She chomps egg. I pour on beans, grate cheese. I cut Sam's toast. 'You mollycoddle that nanny,' Paul says.

'You're stopping me getting a job, you are. How am I supposed to get a job?'

'I'm not stopping you getting a job.'

'You are!' she flashes.

'Sam,' I call, 'lunch.'

He emerges from the playroom with a three-legged plastic dinosaur.

'Raymond wants lunch,' he says.

'Raymond wants a leg,' I remark.

'I shouldn't have told you,' Tessa says, head down. 'I should have just taken him.'

I let this pass. I'm busy trying to balance Raymond on three toenails and a tail.

'I'm too honest.'

'How long does it take at the Job Centre?' I ask.

'What?'

'One hour? Two hours?' I'm about to tell her that prior to going to London next Wednesday I have to go to the hospital for a 10.30 appointment. My private insurance cover apparently expired with my last visit to Baboneau and my GP has now arranged for me to see him at the hospital on the NHS. 'It's possible', I begin, imagining working late the Tuesday night, 'that you could have till 10 on Wednesday morning...'

'10!' She bangs down the bap, bringing Raymond to his knees. 'You don't know nothing, do you!'

'What?'

'You've never done a real day's work in your life, have you?'

'Just because I don't know anything about the internal workings of a Job Centre doesn't mean I've never worked, Tessa. It's not my fault my jobs come through newspapers or contacts or out of my own head.' I say this calmly, coldly. But she knows I'm angry. She realizes, perhaps a moment before I do, that I never normally challenge her.

'You're treating me like shit,' she says.

'Rubbish!' I remember her knife in my ribs.

'Like shit!' she repeats, she shouts.

'I'm just not kid-gloving you today, Tessa, that's all.'

And then in my kitchen, in front of my son, she flips.

'Well, you can stuff your fucking job!' She stands, throws the bap remains and the doughnut into the top of her bag, pulls the drawstring tight and slings the bag like an offensive weapon over her shoulder. She seems to have grown bigger, taller, more solid. I remember how after the moonlighting incident I followed her out of the house to the bus-stop, tried to persuade her back, was afraid that she'd hit me. I'm afraid again. There is a charge in her, a violence.

'I don't have to take this shit from anyone!' She pushes the table with the whole of her body, her will. It moves and with it Sam's plate. Beans and china smash to the floor. My plate stays. Raymond stays. Just. Sam looks at Tessa and then at the floor but doesn't utter a word.

'You can just fuck it! Fuck it!'

I see the tightening in her neck, the clench of muscles in her arms.

97

My heart is beating so fast, so loudly, I think she must surely hear it. I haven't moved from my chair and I'm aware that I must look like a victim. I fear that, like last time, she will put her face close to mine, too close. I hear myself laugh. I think it's a laugh. It sounds strangulated.

'Fuck you!' She slams her body past the dresser, past me, her bag catches cups and they cascade to the floor. But she's in the hall. Thank God she's in the hall.

'If you leave this time,' I say, still sitting, staring straight ahead, 'then you don't come back.'

The front door is wrenched open and then shut in one huge slam of rage. The whole house judders. There is a moment's total silence and then Sam says, 'Tessa's gone then.'

My first thought is, She has my keys; my second that she has worked here for over two years. I find myself on my feet. I can stand. I can walk. I go to the front door and pull the bolt across. It only makes me feel a little safer. I go to the back door and bolt that too, even though there is no back access to our house.

'Raymond doesn't like the mess.' Sam, who is still sitting rigid at the kitchen table, suddenly bursts into tears.

'Baby,' I say and I lift him to me and hug him close. 'It's OK. We'll clear it all up. It'll be fine.'

We get dustpans and brushes and sweep up beans and cup handles and triangular pieces of plate. We clatter and plop them into the bin. I wash the floor. For some reason I Dettox it.

'I'm still hungry,' says Sam.

'Have mine.' I microwave my beans for him and he eats.

I go to the phone and dial Izzy.

She's in. She speaks to me. 'Hello,' she says.

'Izzy, it's me. I have a nanny crisis. Can you help out?'

'I knew a job would come up,' says Izzy.

13

I rearrange my week, agree with Pippa to work Thursday and Friday.

She's sympathetic. 'You poor sod,' she says. 'What a drama.'

I write to Tessa saying I'm sorry things had to end so stupidly after two years. I send her more money than I owe her, wish her well in her next job. 'Sam', I inform her, 'had a big party planned for your leaving. He was going to make you a huge cake.' I know this is rather mean, though not as mean as the kisses I also send from him.

'I'm glad she's gone,' says Paul. 'We should have fired her over the moonlighting a year ago. If anything had happened, I'd never have been able to forgive myself.'

'You don't mind about Izzy coming?'

'Well, it won't be for long, will it?'

The following morning, Wednesday, Dockerills come to change the locks. In the afternoon Sam and I go to meet the 15.45 train. It has taken Izzy a bare twenty-four hours to pack up her life and travel to me. I am impressed with her, in love with her. Grateful. The train is late. Sam climbs on the railings in impatient anticipation and bangs and shakes the ironwork.

'You vandal,' exclaims a ticket collector.

'You Postman Pat,' ripostes Sam.

At 4.01 the train finally curves into view, windows being flung down, doors beginning to open. It snakes into the platform, slows to halt in front of the buffers and the metal boxes full of half-dead geraniums. At once people pour out of the carriages, far more people than might reasonably be expected to be travelling on a mid-October, mid-week, mid-afternoon train.

'Where is she?' yells Sam.

I search the crowds, the outflow of muffled foreign language students who should have flown with the end of the summer; the sauntering black-clad young polytechnic students; the art-school exotics; the old men with donkey jackets, open check shirts and sandwich boxes; the women with buggies, the ample earth mothers, the thin spiky-haired child-mothers; the occasional walking briefcase; the gay clones; the airline pilots; the Gatwick hostesses with their impeccable hats and vanity cases and tans.

'There!' shouts Sam.

And he's right. There she is, right in the thick of the crowd, though I did not see her descend to the platform, a small figure in a shabby, undone navy gaberdine, rucksack half on, half off her shoulder. She walks lazily, though her head is thrust forward, and everyone else just evaporates beside her. I watch the swing of her arms, her too-large glasses, her coming smile and wave as she peers towards us.

'Izzy! Izzy!' As she approaches the barrier, Sam clambers down from the railings.

Izzy stops by the ticket collector and fumbles. Is her ticket in her left pocket? Her right? The top zip of her rucksack? She looks vague, bemused, a clown but I still feel about her as if she'd just ridden down the platform on a white charger. Finally she locates her ticket and comes through the barrier to greet us.

I hold out my arms to hug her, this sister of mine, this shabby saviour who has come to make all things right in my world.

'Don't even think about it,' she says, fending me off and doubling suddenly over her stomach. 'Those British Rail sandwiches, don't they just make you want to retch?'

The spare room bed is made up. There is a pink undersheet, a pink duvet, matching pink pillow cases. The dressing-table is dusted, the drawers empty.

Izzy laughs. 'Thanks,' she says.

I watch her unpack her hairbrush, her make-up bag with the broken zip in which she keeps bracelets and bangles. She lays them on top of the dressing-table with her five-year diary and her Indian ear-rings, she puts her knickers and socks in the top drawer.

I nod and leave her. It's OK. Izzy, who always lives out of her rucksack, intends to stay.

'When I go to work tomorrow,' I tell Sam, 'Izzy's going to look after you.'

'Why?' asks Sam.

'Because Tessa's not coming any more. And because it will be fun. You can go swimming together.'

Sam also nods and leaves.

And so begins a new rhythm in our house. Its beat is surprisingly and comfortingly familiar. I am, I believe, back in control.

The following Wednesday I arrive early for my 10.30 appointment with Baboneau. Thirty minutes early. I've heard that they operate a first-come-first-served policy in this hospital and if I arrive at 10, my notes will take precedence over those of the women with appointments at 10.05, 10.10, 10.15. With luck I will actually get to be seen 'on time', 10.30, and I need the luck. I must catch the 11.46 train to London. I have a lunchtime appointment with a journalist whose feature article is crucial advance publicity for ArtsAid Day.

I push through the dilapidated doors of the hospital. There is no glowingly cheerful private secretary to greet a patient here. In fact, there is no one at all behind the reception desk. I wait, look about me, consider ringing the desk bell. Ring the desk bell. No one comes. I study imaginary writing in the desk top: Charles Brand was here, 1885, 1886 ... still here 1887. Kate Francis woz here ...

'Yes?' The demand from this sudden, *deus ex machina* woman is peremptory but she is not looking at me, she's moving notes, filing, checking the backs of envelopes. My appointment card, held out in the air to her, remains in the air.

'My name's Kate Francis,' I begin. 'I have an appointment with ...'
Her sigh interrupts me. She takes the card.
'Waiting-room 2,' she announces.
'Could you tell me where that is?'
At last she looks up. I see her blue-rimmed, ginger-lashed eyes.
'Down there!'
I follow her wave down the corridor and begin to walk.
'Is this your first time?' she shouts after me.
I return to the desk. 'Yes,' I say. 'At the hospital, anyway.'
'Then you'd better fill in this.' She hands me a four-page form.
'Take a hundred lines,' I say and I smile.
Ginger-lash doesn't smile. It's 10.10.
Recessed to the right of the corridor are two waiting-rooms. They are not labelled 'Waiting-room 1' or indeed 'Waiting-room 2'. Instead, at their wide entrances they have hymn boards which read: 'For patients seeing ...' below which are half a dozen name slots. Today the first room has apparently been designated for patients of Drs Bendy, Mackintosh, Singh and Mr Bute; while the second is reserved for patients of Dr Garfield, Mr Frank and Mr Finsbury.

I stop a nurse in transit in the hall. She's a rather ugly woman in her fifties with corkscrew white hair.

'Which room for Mr Baboneau?' I inquire.

101

'The one which says Baboneau,' she replies.

'Neither of them do.' I'm just beaming.

'They haven't had the time ...' she defends. Clearly she does not have the time either as she proceeds about her business (in and out of blank doors) with no attempt to enlighten me.

I waft in the corridor.

At 10.15, Corkscrew finally pauses by a dump bin, extracts the black-painted name of Mr Baboneau and slots him into the second waiting-room board. Several people in what is now clearly Waiting-room 1 get up and move with the name. Some of them 'tch', most just shake their heads and drift down the corridor, a host of lost souls.

Waiting-room 2, like Waiting-room 1, has green spongey wall seats. I sit, sink and begin my form. Do I smoke? Do I drink? Do I have respiratory trouble, heart trouble, anaemia, diabetes, piles, boyfriend trouble, in-growing toenail? Some of the questions are more complicated: have I had this drug, that drug, this hand up my vagina, that knife in my belly? They should give you this form in a brown paper bag.

'Mrs Francis?'

10.21. Corkscrew moves me to a line of chairs in the corridor. There are two women in front of me and one man. I assume from the man's sheepishness that he's just an appendage and therefore calculate that I must be third in the queue. So I'm still on schedule – just. Corkscrew clumps into the room on our left and, through the briefly open door, I glimpse Baboneau behind a flimsy desk. On my side of the desk a women is weeping. I only see her back view and only for a moment, but I know anyway. The door shuts. I continue with my form. I'm waiting to get to the end, looking forward to the bit where it will say 'other interests'.

Corkscrew comes out and directs the first woman in the queue through a door on the right. Good news! This woman is clearly not even seeing Baboneau. It's almost 10.30. At 10.35 the weeping woman exits Baboneau's. As she passes me, I see that she has a fabulous figure, beautiful curving breasts and hips, long legs, narrow waist, a hanky, a red nose. Corkscrew motions the couple in front of me to take her place.

'Round to the right, Mrs Francis,' she then informs me.

This I do not expect. Is there some other pre-Baboneau procedure?

I gather my form and knock at the door she indicates. Inside the small airless room is a large man in an unbuttoned white coat and, at a side-desk, a small, wizened nurse.

'Sit down,' says the man.

Clearly he is a doctor. But his name is neither on his desk nor pinned to his coat. I sit and wait for him to introduce himself.

'Tell me about your periods,' he says.

He is sitting in front of a large sheet of ruled paper which, but for my name and address, seems to be totally blank. I dither.

'Excuse me,' I say, after a pause, 'I'm very happy to tell you about my periods, but, well ...' I'm pussyfooting. It seems rather rude to say 'in a room not ten yards from here is a man who knows my medical history intimately'. So I fumble: 'Who are you exactly?'

'The registrar,' he says.

'And am I to see you and then Mr Baboneau, or ...' I pause again, waiting for him to jump in, to rescue me. But he says nothing. The silence lengthens into embarrassment. '... or just you?' I conclude finally.

'Just me,' he says.

He still hasn't divulged his name. 'I'm sorry,' I apologize, 'I just haven't been before, here I mean, at the hospital ...'

More waiting. I can see he thinks he's being patient. 'Your periods,' he says.

I begin. 'I was regular, very regular, twenty-eight days exactly, before the birth of my son ...'

'Your son?' he interrupts. 'So you already have a child?'

The sheet is blank. Totally blank. What an absurdity, a waste of time! I should get up, get angry, demand to see Baboneau. So what is it that keeps me pinned to my seat? The fact that this doctor is black. I am consumed with white middle-class guilt. If I ask to see Baboneau, it will look to him (won't it?) as though I am questioning his professional competence.

'What's your name?' I ask hopelessly. I'm almost crying. 'I'm sorry,' I attempt to explain, 'but I find it very difficult to talk to someone who doesn't have a name.' Why can't I just say, 'It puts us on an unequal footing, underlines my inferiority as a patient, as a woman, as a human being who can't conceive?'

He looks at me lazily and I notice the whites of his eyes are streaked with brown. He shakes his head a little and then opens his mouth and makes a noise like water in a hollow tube.

If this is his name (Adewalle? Allullalle? Alulolewe? Alleluyah?) I cannot repeat it nor, so much is my guilt, can I ask him to repeat it. Why isn't it pinned to his breast! I wipe a fist over my eyes. Quarter to eleven, says my watch. I haven't the time to demand, to go back, to wait again in the corridor.

103

'Yes,' I say, 'I have a son.' And I cry.

He writes on the blank form.

'Ninety per cent of women who conceive once conceive again,' he says.

Now I disbelieve him. I hate him. Baboneau has never said this. 'It depends,' was Baboneau's answer to my insistent questioning on this issue. But then why do I believe Baboneau? Why do I persecute myself with the bad news?

'Statistics are rot,' I tell Alleluyah (Dr? Mr? I don't even know that). 'What does it matter if I'm one of the ten per cent who doesn't conceive again?'

He shrugs and writes again on the form.

'Do you have problems with sex?' he inquires.

And so it goes on, through my tears, for twenty more minutes.

'I think we'd better send you for a laparoscopy,' he declares finally.

The wizened nurse begins to swing into action. She reaches for forms, begins scribbling, copying, dating.

'You do know what a 'scope is?'

I do. Oh yes, I do. A laparoscopy is where they cut a hole in your belly button and pass a telescope into your abdominal cavity. They put you under general anaesthethic, blow carbon dioxide into the cavity to 'separate the organs' and then they look. 'Due to the remarkable development of modern optics,' so says my book anyway, 'the view obtained is superb.' The surgeon can inspect your uterus, check to see if your tubes are open, look at your ovaries. Baboneau says there's nothing in my history that suggests the necessity for a 'scope.

'When was the first day of your last period?' Alleluyah inquires.

I tell him.

'That means Day 22 would be . . .' He checks a calendar. 'Friday, 1 November. If we do it in the second half of the cycle then we can also check if you've ovulated.'

'Corpus luteum,' I intone.

'Exactly,' says Alleluyah. He thinks we're friends. The nurse hands him the papers to sign.

'Here you are,' he says, smiling. 'Take them to the clerk.'

'Clerk?'

'Just down the corridor,' says Wizened.

I get up and move to the door, though I've no idea who's pulling my strings. I came to the hospital for a routine chat with Baboneau and I'm leaving with a piece of paper which says that in slightly less than two weeks' time I'll be on the slab and under the knife. And I've said nothing. Nothing about how I don't need the operation, nothing

104

about it being far too close to ArtsAid Day, nothing about how frightened I am. Nothing at all. Except: 'Thank you.'

'Thank you, doctor.'

It's ten past eleven. In the corridor I meet Corkscrew.

'Where's the clerk's room?' I ask.

'What clerk's room?'

I put the papers under her nose.

'Along there,' she points.

The room says 'Office'. I knock and enter.

'Could you wait outside?' The clerk's bored, irritated tone inflames me immediately. Does she think I have X-ray vision, could see through the door that she already had someone with her? I retreat outside and wait. And wait. At a quarter past eleven a man exits and I enter at once, without knocking. The clerk's revenge is to remain, head down, dealing with the man's forms for a good three minutes as I sit and wait. And wait.

Finally, and as though I'm intruding on her most precious work time (can she have any other job than attending to patients?), she greets me.

'Well?'

I hand her the forms.

She sighs and begins more writing, more scribbling, more forms.

'Here,' she thrusts a scrap of white paper at me, 'we've run out of the proper forms for this, but you'll be sent them. The dates are all here.' She points.

'Friday, 25 October,' I read. 'I'm sorry, I thought the doctor said it was to be 1 November?'

With supreme boredom she clicks her tongue and flips the paper. On the back it says '1 November.' 'OK?' she sing-songs, exhausted by my fatuity.

'No. Not OK.' I'm suddenly shaking, the anger all balled inside me. I'm going to howl but I don't care, I'm also going to shout. 'I'm very sorry if all this bores you,' I shout, 'but not being able to have a baby is something that makes me more miserable than anything in my whole life right now. And I come to this hospital and expect to see Mr Baboneau and see some totally different person who doesn't even have the common courtesy to tell me his name before booking me in for an operation which he says is on 1 November but which suddenly appears to be on some totally different date, or maybe it's a second operation no one's told me about and . . .' And basically I rant.

The clerk's tone changes utterly. She reaches for a large box of tissues.

'Is this your first time here?' she asks softly, reasonably.

'Yes,' I say through the tear storm.

'Well, you should have seen Mr Baboneau then. Patients always see him on their first visit. That was very wrong. And didn't they tell you about clerking in?'

'No,' I weep.

'Well, they should have.'

(So should you, so should you.)

'That's not right at all. 25 October for the clerking in, that's when they take all your details so they don't have to do it on the morning of the op. Didn't anyone say?'

I blow my nose.

Someone knocks at the door and begins to enter.

'Could you wait outside?' The clerk's original tone.

Whoever it is recedes.

'And then,' she continues kindly to me, '1 November is the op date. In the Day Case Unit. You see, they don't keep you overnight, which is why they take your details the week before. To speed things up.'

'Look, I can't wait, love.' A man pushes back through the door with two huge bouquets of flowers which he thrusts on top of the clerk's desk. 'Bye, love.' He leaves.

'I didn't know anyone cared,' I whimper.

'Have them,' says the clerk at once. 'They're yours!'

And all of a sudden I know they're funeral flowers.

'No,' I say. 'No thanks.'

'Go on!'

I shake my head.

'They'll only die.' She lays them on the windowsill.

Six tissues later I'm ready to face the world.

The clerk gets up to accompany me to the door. 'Sure you won't have them?' she encourages. 'Just one bunch?'

'I'm going to London,' I say. 'On the train.'

'Oh.'

'Thank you,' I say.

'You're very welcome,' she smiles. 'And by the way, you need to book the blood test at the front desk.'

'Blood test?'

'This one.' She sorts me a piece of paper.

It's 11.25. There is a receptionist at the desk. It isn't Ginger-lash but a dumpy middle-aged woman wearing a uniform so tight it makes her look like a bolster. I hand her the paper and she opens a large book.

106

'What day would you like to come?' she inquires.

'Thursday. Afternoon, if possible.'

'Oh no,' Bolster says. 'We don't do Thursdays. Only Monday, Tuesday or Friday.'

'Then why did you offer me any day!' I scream.

'I didn't offer you any day,' she replies coldly.

'Friday,' I say.

She books me in for 10.30 without asking and, finally, I leave the hospital. I run to the car. It's 11.29 and my train leaves in seventeen minutes. It's a fifteen-minute drive to the station and I don't have a ticket. I roar through the traffic, I take chances I'd never normally take and, with the sort of good luck I've come to regard as the prerogative of other people, I arrive at the station car-park with five minutes to spare. I open my purse. I do not have the two pound coins needed to gain admittance.

'Ah-ah-ah-ah-aaaargh!' I am the lunatic banging his severed head on the roof of the car.

The nearest place to get change is the ticket office, a one-minute walk away. A one-minute walk back. I swerve away from the barriers, I haven't time to park elsewhere. And in any case there isn't an elsewhere by Brighton station. Yes, there is. I see a piece of waste ground I've never noticed before. It looks like some sort of council dump, has skips and a works caravan. Ideal vandal territory. I draw up there and park. Then I run again. The ticket office is mercifully clear. I get my ticket and have two minutes until the train leaves. I also have two pound coins.

Shall I chance it?

I run, get the car, push in the coins, wait the hundred years for the barrier to rise, drive in, take another chance, hang a left, nearest to the station entrance. Will there be a space? Why didn't I look when I was running? Yes, there is one. There is one! I park, handbrake up, doors open, closed, locked. Run. Run. Run.

I'm on the platform, on the train. The whistle blows. I should sit down, take a breath, but I don't. I pound along to the buffet. I order two double whiskies, two American gingers. Then I slump. The whisky spins my head, but not much more than it's spinning already. I'm going to have a laparoscopy.

The book says after laparoscopy rather more women conceive immediately than would be expected by chance. About fifteen per cent more. I drain the whisky. This is a day for beating chance.

14

I make the meeting. The whisky and the adrenalin make me flushed
and bright-eyed. I scintillate. Mike Harding, feature writer, is impressed. I see him admiring my fluency, my verve, my energy. He
flashes back, all smiles and silver pen. Together, over the spritzers, we
make ArtsAid righteous, important, we talk too loudly, we fizz. Our
corner table seems to be the centre of the brasserie, people look our
way, pretending not to. Mike Harding flips the pages of his spiral-
bound notepad, nodding, gesticulating. He thinks I fancy him.

'You understand,' I tell him. 'You really understand.'

'I should have brought a photographer,' he says, his eyes locked on
mine.

'You shameless hussy,' says Pippa when I report back.

'All in a good cause,' I inform her.

I am still glowing when I arrive home. Paul is out at a book launch.
Izzy is curled on the sofa blinking at the television. She looks totally
washed out.

'Kids, aren't they just the hardest job,' I opine. I hear myself say
'kids' plural, when there is only kid singular. Izzy doesn't notice. She
shakes herself like a small dog, switches off the TV and pushes her
glasses further up her nose.

'Hi,' she says. 'How was the hospital?'

My work glow evaporates. I am suddenly centred here, in my
drawing-room, in the warmth of my sister's emotional embrace. I
plant a kiss in her hair, plop myself into an armchair and tell her about
the op. I share the details with her, my hopes and fears. She laughs at
Alleluyah.

'Tell me about your day,' I say, finally, returning the compliment.

'We went to the library twice and to McDonald's once. They were
having a Teddy-bears' Draw-in.'

'McDonald's?'

'The library. You bring your teddy and a kids' illustrator draws it.

Look.' She reaches for a roll of white paper on the adjacent table. 'He was dying to show you this.' It's a caricature of Sandbear, Sam's bean bag teddy. The illustrator has drawn him dancing on a beach, smiling hugely and inanely, one leg poised above a starfish. I feel a stab of jealousy as I look at Sandbear's face, imagine Sam's. I never felt envious of Tessa's time with Sam, but Izzy is doing with my son the things that I would do with him.

'We had to queue for ages. He was really good.' Izzy smiles a little wanly.

'You look like you could use a drink,' I say and I go into the kitchen for wine. We're out of plonk so I take a Chardonnay from Paul's store. I return with two glasses and some ice-cubes.

'Not for me,' says Izzy.

'Don't tell me, you're as snobby as Paul about ice,' I say, pouring myself a large glass.

'Just feel off alcohol.'

'Since when?'

'Since a few weeks, actually. Anyway, I can't afford to booze the way you middle-class couples can.'

'Prole.' I lob a cushion at her.

'Ow! Don't do that!'

'When you were four, you loved a pillow fight.' I grab another cushion, take aim. Cushion fighting is also one of Sam's favourite games.

'Don't,' says Izzy, her arms across her chest. 'It hurts.'

'Rot,' I say putting the cushion down. But I'm pleased to see she's getting old after all.

'Seriously,' she says, 'my breasts.' She waves her hands in front of her. 'They hurt if I so much as think about them today. And Sam's sword!' She draws in her breath.

'Sore tits. Off alcohol. Classic symptoms of pregnancy,' I say. 'You pregnant?'

'Oh sure. Immaculate conception.'

'Must be nice to be celibate,' I muse.

'Grass is greener,' Izzy says, stretching out on the sofa, and putting the thrown cushion behind her head. 'You know it's four and a half months now,' she continues, 'since Martin.'

'You missing him? It?'

'I had a one-night stand.'

'You did?' I stare at my sister. I'm thirty-five years old and I've never had a one-night stand. 'I can't imagine how I'd even begin with

109

someone who wasn't Paul,' I say. 'Not now, anyway. The self-consciousness of it all.'

'Passion', says Izzy, her eyes closed, 'negates the self.'

'Oh? So who was your sex-kitten?'

'No one you know.' She laughs. 'Almost no one I knew. It was rather amazing, actually. A post-Edinburgh indulgence.' She sits up. 'What's the date today?'

'Wednesday, 23 October.'

'Crumbs.' She says it with a little-girl vagueness, as though she's just spilt juice on a not very important dress. 'I may have missed my period.'

'What!'

'I don't know.' She screws up her face, appears to be counting backwards.

'You don't know!'

'Not everyone's as obsessed about dates as you are, Kate.'

'How can you not know!'

She gets up and searches for her bag. 'I'm not very regular. Twenty-nine days. Thirty days. Sometimes thirty-five days. Once I didn't bleed for six months.'

'There.' I point. The bag – black cloth with Latin American trim – is by the fender. She pulls at the drawstring, fumbling for her diary.

'You never had unprotected sex, Izzy.'

She doesn't reply. She's scuffling pages.

'Izzy, you didn't.'

'It wasn't like that.'

'What the hell was it like!'

Her finger comes to rest and she expels a hard breath. Then she tells me.

'It was totally crazy.' At once I see her body stiffen. Normally Izzy's limbs lie lightly, but now her hands are clasping her knees and there is a tension in her neck, around her mouth. Her teeth. 'Totally crazy and totally sane at the same time. A sort of madness where I thought I knew something important that no one else knew and there was no way I could communicate it to them.'

She's just my sister, just sitting on the sofa and yet all of a sudden I can hear the beat of my heart.

'It began in Edinburgh. Jeff's brother got me a press pass and I saw about thirty shows in ten days. It was mad, brilliant. Ideas and emotions knocking in and out of my brain, in and out. And every piece of the theatre seemed to be saying something just to me, for me. Small things, but each one adding, building and then, the night before we were due to come home, I saw Le Space.'

I'm about to speak but she's looking straight through me. I experience my head as a ball of glass. She's talking at me, not to me. Or rather she's talking to herself and I'm not even here.

'This amazing piece' (she hasn't taken a breath) 'by a French Canadian company. No words, just music and fire and people running and walking and passing. Always passing each other. The performance was in a huge space, unlit, growing darker with the dusk. And at its climax two of the characters, a man and a woman, began to walk towards each other. Very slowly, starting at opposite ends of the space. And they were each carrying a torch and singing, Violetta's song from *Traviata*. It was unbearably beautiful and I wanted them to go on singing and walking for ever. And they got closer and closer and I thought, don't stop, don't stop singing. And the whole audience was holding its breath waiting for them to meet, to embrace and they came right within a kiss of each other, and then they walked on, passed each other, never even touching, but singing, still singing. And I thought, that's it, that's what this whole week's been leading up to. It seemed to confirm everything I'd been thinking. What a gift it was to be alive, to have been born, and how I must use that gift, never missing an opportunity to embrace life. To sing and sing but also to touch, never to let anything or anyone pass me by. And after the show I didn't want to say anything to anybody.'

'Some communication.'

'And I didn't say anything,' Izzy continues regardless. 'Not the whole way home in the car.'

And I keep quiet then because she seems to me suddenly like a jug that must pour herself till she's empty.

'It was all too big. Like I couldn't handle it right then. So I just looked out at the night, at the huge empty darkness. All the others slept but I couldn't. And Jeff, who was driving, seemed to know and left me alone. It was 6 in the morning when we arrived back at the flat. Jeff dropped me first and then went to take the others and I think he must have stayed over at Anna's because he didn't come back that day. I was alone in the flat.

'I still didn't feel like sleeping. I just sat in a chair looking out of the window, watching the world wake up, softly, each tree and flower washing into colour. I don't know how long I sat there, I totally lost track of time. I don't think I slept or if I did sleep it was a sort of vision sleep, where I so dreamed of being awake that I was awake. In any case I don't really remember anything else till the afternoon, coming to

111

again and realizing I hadn't eaten for hours. I felt almost beyond hunger but I had a yogurt anyway. One of Jeff's organic ones which had been in the fridge all the time we'd been away. And I imagined the little organisms multiplying inside me, each one simultaneously feeding me and feeding on me. Then I went downstairs to get my bike to cycle into Oxford. But the bike wasn't there. Just the remains of the chain-lock where someone had hacked it through. But I didn't feel angry. Or even annoyed. I just thought fine, this is all part of the meaning. Someone's telling me to slow down, not to bike, to walk. I have to walk. So I started walking. And I saw so much that you don't normally see. I touched the furry undersides of leaves. I smelt the late summer air, seemed to be able to taste the beginning of autumn in my mouth.

'I hadn't set out with any destination in mind but as I walked along I suddenly knew I was going to St Saviour's. I go there quite often, just to walk in the graveyard. I like the way the stones are all broken and the grass has begun to mound over them, like the bodies and the earth are all one. Sometimes I go there hoping to pray but the church is always locked. Well, that day the church wasn't locked. And it all seemed so obvious, so right. I went inside. There was a woman cleaning. Cleaning and singing to herself. And I sat down and watched her clean and listened to her sing and I thought I have never been so happy. Then the sun must have come around the church spire, because suddenly there it was, blazing through the window, a golden rod on the altar. And that was right too. Another symbol specially for me. An untouchable but guiding staff, discovered unexpectedly and yet there for me to see if I chose to look. I stayed in the church till the cleaner left. She was still singing as she locked the door and I had a vision of the song being locked in the church and of it filling the church even though there was no one there to hear it. No one just then, just yet.

'I didn't know where to go then so I just followed the woman for a bit. Not closely, not so as she noticed. Then I realized where she was going. Or at least not where she was going but where she was leading me. To the bench.'

For the first time Izzy pauses. But it is not a pause for breath, it is a pause of amazement. Her own. There's a glaze in her eyes now and if there wasn't an empty glass beside her I'd think she was drunk.

'I've been there before. Just a bench by the road where I sometimes stop, sometimes read, sometimes watch the traffic. But I've also met some amazing people there. So I knew when the cleaner took me past the bench that I'd been guided there, was meant to stop there. So I did. And I waited. And after a while I saw a man fall off his bicycle at the roundabout and at first I thought that was it, that my guide was showing me, that God was showing me, that it could have been me, that if my bike hadn't been stolen I could have fallen off it. Even been killed. And just when I was hugging my luck to me, this man came to the bench and sat down. He was young and dark and wearing pale jeans. He said nothing, for about half an hour he said nothing. But I knew we were supposed to meet, to interact. So after a while I offered him chewing gum and we got talking. He said he had never been to Oxford before, that he was just passing through and needed some-where to stay the night, did I know anywhere? And of course I did, because even if Jeff came back, Tony was still down for the vac so we had a spare room at the flat. He said could we walk it and I said yes, but it would take about an hour and a half. Then he laughed and walked to a car parked at the kerbside. He jiggled with the lock and opened the passenger door. "Not in a car it won't," he said. And I got in.'

'He stole the car!' my middle-class morals suddenly blurt out.

'Yes, I think so. He didn't have a key, didn't start the engine with a key anyway. But that didn't seem important. We got home, parked up...'

'You parked a stolen car in front of your house!'

'... and went in. Jeff wasn't there and I realized then that I knew he wasn't going to be there. But I felt fine about that too, because everything was working right for me and I still had this terrific sense of someone guiding me, looking after me. And this man, whose name was Daniel...'

'Daniel and the Lions' Den – didn't that strike you!'

'Of course, but the den was mine. I'd brought him there. Or God had. And we talked in that very intimate way that strangers often can and I felt that I'd known him all my life and yet I was happy that he was passing through, that I would probably never see him again. And after hours and hours he said he had to go to bed, so I showed him Tony's room and he just said, "Thanks." I stayed up, read poetry. Then, at about one, he came to my room with one of Tony's towels round his waist and said he couldn't sleep for thinking of me and could we make love. And I looked at him, white and hairless despite the darkness of his facial hair and I said no. I don't know why I said no, it wasn't any more thought out than anything else that day, it just seemed like the right response. He didn't push it at all. Didn't try and persuade me – just accepted it and went back to Tony's room. Then I couldn't sleep. Wondered why I'd said no to that when I'd said yes to everything else that day. Why should I be holding back about sex, about touching, about the very embrace that Edinburgh had seemed designed to show me was right? And for a second night, I didn't sleep, I meditated, I prayed. I asked for another sign to show me the way. And in the morning there had been no sign and then it came to me that the absence of a sign *was* the sign. That I could only be guided so far, that now I had to trust, to have faith. I went to his room and told him I was ready.'

'Please tell me you took a condom.'

'I looked in my drawer but I didn't have any.'

'Izzy!'

'And I told Daniel and he said it didn't matter because he was infertile.'

'Oh, for fuck's sake! You never believed that!'

'Of course I believed it. Why shouldn't I have done? Anyway, I thought it was part of the test. Part of the trust I had to come to terms with.' She looks up at me. 'So we did it. Made love.'

'I hope it was good!'

'Yes, it was good. Very gentle. Me coming awake like I'd seen the world coming awake the morning before.'

'Jesus Christ.'

'And it was morning again then. And afterwards I said I'd make breakfast and Daniel said he'd get papers. While he was out I made toast. There was only one egg and I boiled it for him. Then I laid the table and as I laid it I knew I wanted flowers. So I went down on to the street to where there is this wall which has briar roses over it and I picked a whole armful of pink roses. Brought them back and arranged them in a milk bottle. They were really beautiful. Then I sat down to wait for him.'

'Don't tell me he didn't come back.'

'He didn't come back. But I didn't mind, Kate. That seemed right too. A fit ending. I'd laid the table for Christ. The perfect lover.'

'Fucking hell.' I'm shaking so hard I can barely stand but I do stand. Anger bolts my legs. I go upstairs and get a Clear Blue pregnancy testing kit from my dressing-table drawer. You just piss on the dipstick and if there's a blue line in the larger window two minutes later, you're pregnant. I return downstairs and give the tester to Izzy.

She stands too. She's no longer stiff at all, but loose and dreamy. She almost floats out towards the loo. Two minutes later she's back. She lays the stick on the table between us. There is a blue line in the larger window.

I get up, cross to the sofa, and hit her full in the face.

15

The next morning my sister is gone. On the spare-room dressing-table is the dust outline of her make-up bag, her bangles. The bed is pulled over, the duvet plumped and neat.

'What did you expect?' Paul says.

'She's supposed to be my nanny. She took the job.'

'I don't think you'll find an employer's right to beat an employee enshrined in any law in this country.' Paul is shaving, mixing soap in a wooden bowl, lathering his chin with Geo Trumper Limes. I'm sitting on the edge of the bath.

'How can she be so clever and so stupid at the same time?'

He lifts his razor. 'How can she be so fertile, you mean.'

'That's not fair!'

'Isn't it?' He draws the blade down from his ear.

'She might have got Aids.'

'Oh, please.' He swashes the razor in the basin, already the water looks grey.

'I mean, what did she think she was doing?'

'What Izzy always does. Letting her life wash over her.'

'That's not fair either.'

He pauses, razor in mid-air: 'Face it, Kate, this time your sister's really gone and done it.'

Sam sticks his head round the door. 'You're a poo-pax, Dad,' he says, giggles and disappears.

'And for once I don't think God will be coming to the rescue,' Paul continues, bringing the blade close to his mouth. 'Seeing how He's the one who's mainly got her into this.'

'You don't care at all, do you?'

'Me? Don't point the finger at me. You're the one who belted her.'

'I was shocked.'

'You were jealous!'

I get off the bath.

115

'I have to go to her.'

'Don't you dare.'

'She's going to need someone. Need me.'

'In the circumstances, Kate, I think you're about the last person she's going to need right now. I mean, think of it from her point of view – talking abortions with someone who's currently failing to conceive . . .'

'Who said anything about abortions?'

He lays down the razor. 'Kate, if she needed you she wouldn't have left, would she?'

An hour later Paul is at work, Sam is at school and Julia is on standby. As I collect my car keys, I hear on the local radio that a baby has been found on the steps of Brighton General Hospital. It's a girl, weighing 6lb 2oz and wearing a bin-liner. They've called her Hope after the nurse who found her. I'm still laughing about this when the door bell rings. It's Tessa.

'I done wrong,' she says.

I look her in the eye. Hard. Her right eye is a blob of blood. The socket is bruised and there is no white on her eyeball at all, only red. The sight is brutal and sickening.

'Who did it to you?' I feel a rage, a protectiveness, I think my voice wobbles.

She shrugs. 'It's a lot better than last week,' she says, 'when they done it.'

I look at my watch, my car keys. 'You'd better come in,' I say. I take her into the kitchen, sit her down and make her a cup of tea.

'What happened?'

'I can't tell you.'

'Tessa, you haven't come all the way round here not to tell me, have you?'

'You wouldn't understand.'

'Tessa, I'm very busy.'

'I miss Sam,' she says.

'And he misses you,' I lie.

'Have you got someone . . . ?'

'Yes, my sister. Have you come round for your old job?'

'No.'

'What then?'

'I done wrong. I knew I done wrong the minute I left the house.'

I take this as an apology. Tessa has never been able to apologize. I

116

think it's because she was so often wrongly accused as a child that she's now sealed herself against all blame, deserved or not.

'It's OK,' I say. 'It's fine. Doesn't matter.'

Her tea is untouched. She sits and sits.

'Tell me who did it?'

'Why?' she asks. 'What you going to do to them?'

'Nothing. Though the police might. It's called Grievous Bodily Harm.'

'You ain't seen nothing.' She pulls down her pink fluffy jumper. On her right breast is a bruise the size of a fist. It's purple and orange.

'Jesus.'

'And on my legs,' she says, 'and my back.'

'Go to the police.'

'You got to be joking.'

'Hitting people is wrong,' I say.

Tessa laughs. 'I hit her first.'

'Tell me, Tessa!' I shout.

'I can't.'

I shake my car keys. 'Right,' I say, 'I'm going.'

Like a dog she follows me to the front door. I lock it behind us.

The drive to Oxford takes an hour and a half. I take the Cowley exit from the ring road. I don't know Izzy's actual street but I am familiar with the general grimy area and I find her house without trouble. As I park up, I wonder what was going through Daniel's mind as he parked up in the stolen car: Bet my luck's in tonight. The house is set back from the road, largish and unkempt. The Edwardian sills are grey and peeling, the guttering loose. I see the autumn leaves that Paul would see if he were here, how they're blocking a drainpipe and causing a smear of damp down the grey façade. I lock the car and hope the radio will still be in it when I return. There are four wide grey steps to the door and the top step is inset with terracotta and powder blue tiles. The geometric corners are missing. On the left-hand side of the door are three bells. Flat 2 is occupied by Turney, Francis and Watts, or so it says in biro beneath the wet, lifting sellotape. I press and wait. I am prepared to wait. If necessary I shall sit like Izzy on the doorstep. After a time I press again and then, because I can't hear the bell, knock as well. A window opens on the second floor.

'Hello?'

It's a male voice. I step back so I can see him and he can see me. It's

117

11.45 on a coldish October day. The man is wearing a white T-shirt
and his thick blond hair falls in his face. He looks as if he's just got
up.

'Jeff?' I hazard.

'Yeah?'

'I'm Kate, Izzy's sister.'

'Oh.'

'Is she in?'

'Don't know. Don't think so. Why don't you come up and see?
Door's open.'

I push the door. It is open. How did he know? Is it always open?
And how does he know I'm Izzy's sister? Maybe I don't look like a
burglar. In the hall there is a cheap beige carpet. It is not fitted and it
slides a little when I step on it. There are also two bikes, one of them
chained, a black rubbish sack with a dribble of baked beans down it
and, on the floor, about a year's spew of junk mail.

'Up here.'

I follow the disembodied voice up the stairs. The stairwell has that
peculiar fungoid bed-and-breakfast smell that triggers instant depression in me. The door to the flat is open but Jeff is not there to greet
me. I go in. The inner hallway is dark, but not so dark that I can't see
that it's a long time since the carpet (olive green) has been swept.
There are more black bags here. These ones seem to be full of clothes,
the stiff and sweaty sort you wouldn't even bother to send to a jumble
sale. I begin to feel old.

'Jeff?' I call. 'Izzy?'

As there is no reply, I head for the greatest source of light, the grey
chink of a slightly open door.

'Hello?'

It's the drawing-room. There are two upright chairs, a table, a
mattress sofa spread with an Indian cloth and some floor cushions.
Each item of furnishing, such as it is, is covered with a thin layer of
grey dust. Ash. There is also ash in the ashtrays, and cigarette butts in
various cups and mugs. On the table yesterday's dinner – I'd guess at
vegetarian curry – is congealing and though there are only two empty
beer cans the room smells of stale alcohol. On the windowsill which
looks over the garden are a number of healthy-looking pot plants. I
wonder if they are pot, squeeze the leaves. They're lemon geranium.

'Izzy's room's round the back.' Jeff emerges from a door to my right
carrying coffee. I get a glimpse of the room behind. Jeff would
probably call it the kitchen.

'Thanks.' Clearly he has not checked whether or not Izzy is in. I

118

follow his vague point back out into the hall and down a dark corridor. I knock on a door.

'Izzy?' There is no answer. I push the door open. It's the bathroom. If there used to be enamel on the bath there isn't now. The steel taps are corroded and one of them is leaking. Automatically I try to turn it off. It won't be turned. The hot water boiler creaks and sways a little as I pass. I can't imagine that it delivers hot water. This is the sort of room which can never be warm, not least because it hasn't got a radiator. There is also a triangle of glass missing from the window pane. When it snows, I imagine they will stick up a piece of cardboard. I crack my way back over the brittle lino and out into the hall again.

One more blank door. I knock. There is no reply, but I'm not expecting a reply now. I go in. This is indeed Izzy's room. Izzy never makes much impression on the communal rooms of the houses in which she lives, but her bedroom is always quintessential Izzy. There's colour here – Latin American pink and black and yellow, Indian green and blue, clothes, beads, cloth. There are some mimimal comforts, a cushion, an Oxfam rug, her old, adapted, red velvet curtains. There are books and plants, a desk, pictures on the wall, colourful posters and water-colours she's painted herself. One of the posters, Millais' *The Blind Girl*, used to be mine. The older girl is blind, the younger girl (in her arms) is looking at a rainbow. I don't know when I began to find it sentimental. There are also photos. Photos of the places Izzy has been and the people she loves. There are two photos of me. The first one was taken on the beach at Tenby. I'm sixteen and wearing a lime green bikini. She's eighteen months and paddling frantically across the sand towards me in a pink seersucker costume. My arms are outstretched. I can't imagine my mother taking this picture but I suppose she must have done. The second photo is more recent. It's of me sitting in my garden at home eating water-melon. It's the summer and I'm smiling but you can't see the smile, only the grin of the water-melon rind. Izzy took this picture herself.

'You shouldn't have come.' Izzy is suddenly standing in the door-way, watching me watching her.

I wheel about. 'I'm sorry,' I say immediately.

Izzy says nothing. She's got her coat on and she's wearing a huge pair of mirror dark glasses.

'I shouldn't have hit you. It was stupid. It was wrong.' I pause. 'I done wrong.' I attempt a smile.

Still nothing. She takes off her coat and sits down at the desk chair. She does not take off the glasses.

'Izzy . . .'

119

'Don't,' she says. 'Just don't.'

I waver a little. 'Have you come from St Saviour's?' I ask.

She tilts her head and I see a small, a tiny, easing in her shoulders. 'Yes,' she says.

'And?'

She picks up a stone from the desk, a polished piece of snowflake obsidian, smooths it between her finger and thumb. 'It was locked.'

'But you heard the song,' I say, 'the song that's still inside.'

'Kate ...' she warns.

'I've only come to see how you are,' I say quickly. 'How you feel.' Her palm is open and she's staring at the stone, its blackness lit with a powder fall of white. 'How do you feel?'

'Like a woman.' She lifts her head and laughs suddenly, her summer sunshine laugh. 'Didn't know that before. Before I felt like a person. Now I feel like a woman.'

This is safe ground. 'And what does a woman feel like?'

'Special. Secret. Abundant. Fertile.' Her mouth turns irresistibly up. 'Sorry,' she adds.

'No need to be.'

'I mean, didn't you feel it with Sam?' She can't stop her own exuberance, her Izzyness. 'That magic, that your body works, that you can contain life?'

'Yes,' I say but my voice is dull.

She shrugs, shaking the mood from her. 'And, if you really want to know, I also feel shocked, frightened and confused.'

'Confused?' I gather the word quickly. 'Surely not confused?'

'You ought to go,' she says.

'Have you told Jean?'

'Of course not.' She puts down the stone, locks her head and turns her silver gaze on me. 'This is something I have to work out for myself, Kate. For myself. By myself.'

The door is closing. 'But you don't have to work it out at all, Izzy, do you?' I say precipitately. 'I mean, do you? I mean, what's there to work out? It's all obvious. As obvious as that shaft of light was on the altar. That guiding staff.'

'Kate ...'

'I mean, what else could it mean? That whole day? That whole extraordinary day? The gift of a child.' She's putting her hands up to her ears now, as if she would cover them, as if she would block me out. But she can't block me out because she knows me too well, knows what I'm going to say even before I say it. 'Carry the child for me, Izzy!'

120

'You're mad,' she says. 'You're crazy!' But she says it too fast and her voice is too high.

'I'm only mad if everything you've ever believed in is mad, Izzy. Everything you've ever wanted, experienced. Go with the swim, Izzy. Respond, respond.' I'm moving nearer to her, a step nearer. I can see myself in her glasses.

'No!' Now she stretches out her hands, spreads her fingers, pushing the air hard against me. 'No.'

'I'm saying you're right, Izzy. All these years I've planned and planned, tried to control things. Well, that's the madness, Izzy, you said so yourself. Ease up, you said. Be spontaneous. Open yourself up to whatever life presents you with. Well, life's presenting me with a child, Izzy. Your child. Our child.'

'My child. Mine!'

I've come too near, tripped her. 'Izzy . . .'

'Leave me alone!'

'You can't abort. You mustn't.'

She's pushing herself up, standing. Her face is brilliant white. 'Doesn't it even occur to you that I might want the child for myself? For itself?'

'For itself? Here?' I'm suddenly gesturing wildly. 'In this flat? In your life? Your lunatic, wayward life! You can't let things just drift when you have a child to consider!'

She laughs, A throttled sound. 'You're unreal,' she says.

'A child is work, it's commitment. It's rootedness.'

'You think I don't know?'

'I think you don't know.'

'I would love the child, Kate.'

'And I would love it. Give it a home. A brother. A family.'

'I know that too.' Now she's whispering.

'Izzy . . .'

'Go away.'

But I'm moving towards her, snatching the dark glass from her white, white face. I'm looking into her huge beautiful eyes. They aren't bruised but they are inflamed. The dry red eyes of someone who has cried for so long the salt has burnt her.

'Oh Izzy, my Izzy.' I put my arms up to hold her.

But she will not be held.

16

Two hours later I'm back in Brighton. Tessa is sitting on my doorstep, the collar of her black leather jacket pushed up against the wind.

'No,' I say. 'Whatever it is Tessa, no.'

'I come to tell you,' she says.

I unlock the door. She looks up at me but she doesn't move. Maybe she can't, maybe she's frozen to the doorstep.

'How long have you been waiting?'

She shrugs. 'Two hours. Three.' This is not plaintive, merely matter-of-fact.

'Come in,' I say. I lead her straight to the kitchen. I don't take her coat but I do make a pot of tea. I need a cup and her hands at least look as if they could use the warmth.

'Shoot,' I say.

There is a pause.

'In twenty-five minutes,' I say, 'I have to collect Sam.'

She looks out of her bloodshot eye at me.

'I'm one of them,' she confesses.

'What? One of what? One of whom?'

'Them people you read about in the papers.'

'What people?'

'You know.'

'Tessa, I'm not clairvoyant.'

'The ones you said live on islands and write poetry.'

'Lesbos? Lesbians?'

She nods. 'I hate that word.'

Tessa is full of surprises but this one lays me flat. Tessa – a lesbian! It makes perfect psychological sense of course: her father beat her mother, she was raped when she was nine (pinch of salt, says Paul) and she certainly didn't have a boyfriend in the two years she worked for us. But big, blonde, short-skirted Tessa! I recall the poetry and islands conversation. Tessa was reading the *Sun* and got stuck on 'that word':

122

'Les ... les ... les ... I hate that word.' At the time I blamed her dyslexia and imagined, with supreme middle-class liberal arrogance, that what she actually hated was lesbianism itself. To school her from her tabloid morals I told her about Sappho. And now here she is in my kitchen, with her black leather jacket, pink lipstick and battered eye, telling me she's the thing itself. Who's blind and who sees the rainbow?

'Filthy dyke,' she says. 'That's what Mum calls me.'

'Charming.' I'm not up to saying much more. I'm too shocked. This is obviously my week for being shocked.

'It's 'cos of Ken. That's what he says.'

I've noticed how Tessa lays most of the blame for her mother's faults at her mother's boyfriend's door. Such faults as she admits her mother has. Maybe Tessa has too few people to love her, to fall out of love with her mother? 'My Mum's the best in the world,' that's what she was always telling me. A mother who didn't ask her nine-year-old child why she was late on the day she was raped. A mother who calls her a 'filthy dyke'. Blood can be thick enough to choke you.

'So what does being a lesbian have to do with being beaten up?'

'I only wanted a cuddle,' she says.

'That's pretty much all that any of us want.' To be held. To hold. My own arms still feel Izzy's unyielding body as a bruise.

'Only she don't see it.'

'She?' I question.

'Rosemary. My – you know.'

'Flatmate. Soulmate. Lover. The Older Woman. OAP-snatching.'

She looks at me. 'You're weird, you.' There's nothing judgemental in her tone.

'Sorry,' I say, 'I interrupted. Rosemary didn't see the cuddles the way you did...?'

'She wanted to go to bed by herself sometimes. But I wanted to go with her. Not to do anything. Just to cuddle.'

(Oh Izzy, my Izzy.)

'And she found that oppressive.'

'What?'

'She wanted more personal space?'

'You talk like a crossword, you.'

'OK, you tell me, what did she want?'

'I think she wanted Barbara.'

'Barbara?'

'The woman, you know, before me.'

'Is that what the thirty-two paracetamol were about?'

123

'Barbara would have her back. I know she would. I seen them together when they don't know I seen them.'

'You follow them?'

'Sometimes. They ain't never seen me though.'

'How long did Barbara have her for?' I am using Tessa's language of possessiveness.

'Ten years.'

'Ten years! And how long has she been gone?'

'Two months. But she's OK.'

'How do you mean, "OK"?'

'Got over it.'

'Would you get over a ten-year relationship in two months?'

'Don't be stupid. I never had a ten-year relationship.' Imaginative empathy is not Tessa's strong point. But then why should it be? Who has compassion for her?

'Jealousy is corrosive,' I say. 'It makes you utterly unlovable.'

'I don't know what you mean – jealous?'

'I mean like when your sister is going to have a baby and you're not.'

'I don't have no sister,' says Tessa.

'I mean, if you were less obsessed about Barbara, maybe Rosemary would want to hold you more, cuddle you more.'

'She does cuddle me now,' says Tessa. 'It's all right now, since they done it.'

'Bloody but unbowed.'

'You feeling all right?' Tessa asks.

'Just a bit drunk.' I laugh. 'Punch drunk.' Arms to hug and arms to hit.

'I was sick as a dog,' commiserates Tessa. 'That and the blood. Yuck. You should have seen my sheets. I had to throw them all away. And the duvet.'

'Barbara beat you up in bed?'

'Not Barbara! Why do you say Barbara? It was Rosemary's friends.'

'Rosemary's friends? Her friends! And where was Rosemary the while?'

'In the front room.'

'Tessa, I think you'll have to go back a bit for me.'

'I went down the pub. You know, where she got me the job. That was after a really bad night. We was rowing and rowing and she wouldn't hold me. She wouldn't even touch me. And I was shouting, "I only want a cuddle. Only a cuddle!" But she wouldn't. Didn't even never say goodbye to me when she went out to work. I went down the pub and smacked her in the face. All her friends was there, they saw it.'

'So they came round and beat you up to even things up?'

'It weren't the first time I hit her.'

'And Rosemary just let them.'

'She couldn't do nothing about it. There were six of them.'

'Six!'

'Two of them held me down and the others kicked me. Punched me. You should have seen the blood on the pillow.'

'Rosemary must have let them in.'

'No, she never.'

'Well, somebody must have done.'

Tessa shrugs. 'They would have got in anyhow.' There is something in her simple acceptance of the way things are, the way they have to be, which makes me ashamed. Moment to moment, Tessa lives her harsh life. She does not complain. Why doesn't she complain?

'And while you're screaming blue murder Rosemary's just sitting in the front room?'

'I wasn't screaming. Kevin had his hand over my mouth.'

'Oh – the shining white knight.'

'Yeah. He was the only boy. He did it so the neighbours wouldn't hear.'

'Nice friends you've got.'

'Not my friends. Rosemary's.'

'What made them stop?'

'When I was sick. I sicked on Kevin's hands. And there was blood all running from me nose. Pouring down my face. I think it scared 'em. They let me up. Then I went into the front room and said, "Look what they done to me, Rosemary!" But she had her head in her hands and she wouldn't look. But I pulled her hands away. I made her look. I made her.'

'And what did she say?'

'Didn't say nothing. Cuddled me.' There is no look of triumph on Tessa's face, just a surprise, a gratefulness. 'She got rid of them. Then she washed me. Put me to bed in her bed. I was sick again. Twice. Three times. I can't remember. But she didn't care. She just held me. She cuddled me.'

'Why have you come to tell me all this, Tessa?'

'Dunno,' she says and then she shrugs. 'I guess you gotta tell someone.'

And although I know she needs no pity, I get up and hold her too.

125

17

'Postman Pat', says Paul, coming downstairs later that evening, 'is a half-wit.'

'You're not three years old,' I comment from the stove. I rather resent Sam's current preference for his father to read him his bedtime story. Paul thinks it's because of my disinclination to cook.

'What's for supper?' he asks.

'Pasta.'

'Oh.' This is Paul's perennial reaction to pasta, as if pasta is a non-food, or I'd said, 'Best coal.'

'Why did you open the Chardonnay?' He's staring in the fridge.

'Because we're out of plonk.'

'No, we're not.' He goes to the cupboard under the stairs and rearranges boxes. 'There's a whole crate of the stuff.'

A few minutes later he's sitting at the kitchen table with some Bordeau Blanc and a bottle of Crème de Cassis, stirring himself a huge kir.

'Bad day?' Paul often drinks kir when he's depressed. It reminds him of better times, hotter suns, other countries.

'Don't ask.'

I don't ask. I chop *pomodori secchi*.

'How about you?'

'Tessa came round.'

'Oh?'

'Told me she was a lesbian.'

'You're kidding.'

'Straight up.' I relay Tessa's story.

'She's a one-woman social statistic, that girl. *Guardian*'s wimmin's page could have a field day.'

'Do you know what makes me really sad?'

'What?'

'The thought that she probably won't have a child of her own.'

126

'Lay off, Kate. That's your obsession. She probably doesn't give it the time of day.'

'I really think it would centre her, give her a purpose. Think how she loved Sam. Loves Sam. And she's such a lot of love to give.'

Paul reaches for the paper. 'Well, you don't need a man to get pregnant. Ask your sister. One quickie down the pub and hey presto – another fatherless child.' He turns to foreign news. I open a tin of anchovies.

'Where did you learn to be so unpleasant?'

'Comes naturally to a rational man living in a irrational age.' He's reading about Moldavia. For a while there's a silence which sizzles with garlic and tomatoes and capers and red pesto, then he says, 'Did you have to work?'

'What?'

'I said, did you have to work?'

'No.'

'Then why did Sam go to Julia's?'

'Ah.' I try to bury the pause in the hiss of gas from the grill. Paul likes his plates very hot.

'When I was putting him to bed,' Paul says, 'he told me he went to Julia's.'

'William's his best friend,' I say.

'It's Thursday,' Paul states. 'One of your days with your son.'

I turn to face my husband. 'I went to Oxford,' I say.

'You what?'

'Went to Oxford.'

'Jesus Christ, Kate, why don't you join the Samaritans?'

'Izzy is my sister.'

'I'd noticed.' He pours himself another kir.

'Who's she supposed to talk to?' I ask him.

'Her mother?'

'Do me a favour.'

'Her friends. Her GP. The British Pregnancy Advisory Service. Or even – strike me dead – the father of her child?'

I stir oil into the pasta water. 'She's not having an abortion, if that's what you think.'

'What is she going to do then? Pray?'

'I think she wants to keep the child.'

'What!' Paul sputters into his wineglass. 'She's crazy.'

'That's what I said.'

Paul looks up, the sneer gone from his face. 'Good for you, Kate.'

I turn my back on him and reach for the black pepper. 'I said it

127

would be much more sensible if we had the child.' My hand trembles in the pause. I wait. I imagine his face, the shocked disbelief giving way to ... laughter. He *laughs*.

'Ingenious,' he says.

I go to the store cupboard and get a bottle of whisky. I pour myself a large glass and sling in two ice-cubes.

'I'm serious,' I say. I face him. He can see my eyes.

'Oh, fine then,' he says. 'Easy peasy. Sure thing.' He lifts his glass. 'Great idea. Cheers. And thanks for including me in on discussions, by the way.'

'I was going to tell you. Ask you. Discuss it. I haven't seen you till now.'

'Well, there really isn't that much to discuss, is there? Besides, what's a man? What's a father's, what's a bloody husband's opinion got to do with anything?'

'Paul ...'

'No, Kate!' He flips the paper shut and bangs it flat with his fist. 'We are not having Izzy's bastard. Not now. Not never. Finito. End of story.'

'How can you say that?'

'Easily.'

' "Bastard", how can you say "bastard" about your own flesh and blood?'

'Your flesh and blood. Not mine. Yours, or rather Izzy's, and that of some two-bit fuck-artist on a bench!'

I drain the pasta. I should have waited. Why can I never wait? I was going to wait but he caught me out – or Sam did. I pour on the sauce, add parsley. The plates are piping hot. I serve at the stove and bring Paul his, offer him Parmesan cheese and a grater. I get out cutlery and sit down beside him.

'If you adopt,' I say, 'you might get the child of two two-bit fuck-artists on benches.' I smile winningly. 'This way we at least know the provenance of one half.'

'I don't want to adopt,' says Paul simply.

This astonishes me. Paul and I have not discussed adoption but my secret heart has always assumed that we think similarly on the subject – that is, if we have to adopt, we will.

'Why not?'

'Because I could never love someone else's child as much as Sam.' He states this as if it is an eternal truth, then he grates cheese.

'But why?'

'Because I couldn't.'

128

'That's not a reason.'

'Kate, Sam's my son. This other child ...' he waves his fork, '...
wouldn't be.'

'That's irrational.'

'Hardly,' Paul says. 'I think you'll find Darwin bears me out, not to
mention a millennium or so of basic evolutionary biology.' He eats.

I don't eat, my appetite is gone. After a while he relents, lays his
hand on mine.

'Anyway, we're going to have another child of our own.'

'Are we?' Normally his confidence mollifies me, makes me feel
strong. But tonight it's too easy and there's too much at stake. 'Are we
really?'

'Well, you're taking the herbs, aren't you?'

'Don't mock.'

'I'm not mocking. I only said, you're taking the herbs. And then
there's Izzy's bones ...'

I don't know if he's mocking or not. I take a large slug of whisky and
get up to refill my glass.

'And then the laparoscopy, of course ...'

'What if they find something the size of a pineapple?'

'It'll be good news,' says Paul. 'They can cut it out.'

'Thanks.' I push away my plate. 'What if they find I'll never be able
to conceive again?'

'They won't.'

'But what if they do?'

He lays down his knife and fork. 'Then maybe we just have to be
grateful we have Sam.'

He's never said this before. It sounds so final. He sounds so
unmoved. 'So you'd rather have no child than Izzy's child?'

'I said finito, Kate.'

'You would, wouldn't you?'

'Yes, OK, I would. How can I make it plain to you?' He's beginning
to shout. 'I don't want Izzy's bastard. OK? Is that clear enough for
you? I don't want Izzy's bastard.' He calms down a little. 'Anyway,
who says she's offering?'

'If she did,' I say, getting up to scrape my leavings into the bin.
'And she might.'

'What are you going to do, Kate? Go to the hospital and rip it out of
her arms? You know what you feel when a baby's born, Kate, you of all
people. Be practical, for God's sake.'

'Practical!'

'Yes, practical. What's wrong with practical?'

'The practical solution would be for Izzy to abort.'

'Precisely so.'

'And where does that leave the baby?'

'Out of it, I'd say.' Calmly he stands up, calmly he helps himself to more pasta.

'None of it's the baby's fault.'

'I never said it was.'

When I was a student I went on abortion marches: a woman's right to choose. Since Sam, I feel quite differently and although I probably wouldn't rally to the side of pro-Life, I do think of each unborn foetus as a child. Or perhaps I *feel* each unborn foetus as a child. I imagine all the things that child might do or be. I think, who has the right to say another's life is not worth living, is not to be lived? I would feel this if I conceived a handicapped child, that that child should still be. At least I think I would feel this. Hope I would.

'If you have love to give,' I ask Paul, 'what does it matter whose baby it is?'

'It matters to me.'

'Why?'

'How many times do I have to tell you? If I'm going to be a father, that's what I want to be – the father.'

'So it's all down to your prick?'

'Give it a rest, Kate.'

'Well, it is, isn't it? If it's not your precious sperm, then that's it.'

'OK, Kate, yes. Yes. Yes. Yes. If that's the way you want to put it. Yes. Satisfied?'

His smile infuriates me. The red pesto smear round his mouth infuriates me.

'How do you know for sure Sam's your son?'

'Don't be stupid.'

'What's stupid about that?'

There is a smug twist to the red pesto. 'I know Sam is my son because you conceived him in the days when you were reasonable.'

'Reasonable!'

'Yes. Reasonable. Are we going to have a semantic discussion about "reasonable" now?'

'You tell me what's reasonable!' I'm shouting now. 'Your stupid, stupefying notions of some hereditary paternity or my simple desire to love a child which is already on the way?'

He stands up. 'Kate, it is not your child!'

'What does it fucking matter whose child it is!'

'It matters to me.'

'But . . .'

'But nothing, Kate. But absolutely fucking nothing! Now just shut up, will you? Just shut up.'

'No, I won't shut up! Why should I shut up? You shut up!'

'Fine by me.' He shuts up.

But I haven't finished yet.

'You're the one who's supposed to be so reasonable,' I shout. 'So *rational*. So why don't you use that brilliant, logical brain of yours for once and just work it out. Work it out! We want a child. She has a child. Bingo!'

'You want a child,' Paul says.

And there it is. Boomph. All the air punched from my chest. And I've driven him to it. I've forced him to say this one unsayable thing. It's entirely and only my fault.

'I hate you,' I scream.

Into my scream comes a clattering, a rumbling as if something totally uncoordinated is falling, falling. For minutes it falls, from the top of the house to the bottom. Then there is a thud at the foot of the stairs and Sam appears, picking himself up off the tile floor.

'Stop doing it to each other,' he screeches.

And we stop. Our son's face is bathed in tears.

Paul reaches Sam first. 'Poppy,' he says and gathers his son to him. Sam sobs against Paul's chest, his gangly legs tight around his father's waist.

'It's OK,' I say to Sam's back, 'it's OK.' I ache to hold him but Paul is holding him. So I touch his head, stroke the flesh of his legs where his pyjamas have ridden up.

'I'll take him up,' Paul says softly. There is sadness and anger in his eyes. The anger is for me.

I follow the pair of them up the stairs watching Sam's body quieten; his limbs ease, his head heavies, his body folds into his father's. As we go into his bedroom, Sam's night-light flickers. Paul nods at me, motioning me towards Sam's duvet. I lift back Postman Pat and Paul lowers Sam gently on to the sheet. Sam wriggles and turns.

'Mummy,' he says.

I pull the duvet over him and sit down on the edge of the bed. I take his hand.

'Mummy,' he says again. His eyes are half closed.

I lean down and hold him, kiss him. He never calls me Mummy.

'It's OK,' I tell him. 'You're a good boy. I love you.' In the doorway Paul snorts. 'And Daddy loves you too,' I say.

Daddy exits.

'And I love Daddy,' I whisper. I stroke his cheek. 'It's all OK.'

He rubs at his eyes and snuffles, moving his head beneath my hand. Then he grabs at my fingers and pulls my hand from his face. His eyes open just as the night-light flickers a second time. For a moment I look into his huge brownness and then there is a fizz and the room turns black.

Instantly awake, Sam screams, 'Turn it on!' And his hand panics round mine.

'It's OK,' I say.

'Turn it on! Turn it on! Turn it on!'

I try to calm his hands, still his mouth. I hold his arms to his chest.

'I don't think it's the light-bulb,' I say. The hall seems black. The corridor seems black. 'I think it's a power-cut.'

He's fighting me now, trying to sit up.

'Calm down!' He winds himself round my body, begins to cry into my neck. 'Don't be silly,' I say. 'It's only a power-cut.'

'What's a power-cut?' he wails.

'Well,' I begin calmly and rationally, 'all the lights in our house are powered by electricity ...' I hold him, murmur at him, making everything sound normal, ordinary. 'And if we don't have any lights, then nor does anyone else,' I conclude. 'Would you like to look out of the window and see if anyone else has lights?'

His eyes have begun to grow accustomed to the dark and his grip on me has loosened.

'OK,' he says.

I lift him to the window and push aside the bird of paradise curtains. Every house in our street is black. The earth is black. But hung in the sky, so close it might be over our garden, is a huge, shimmering moon. I have never before seen this shadow-sun so white, so scintillating. Perhaps I have never looked.

'Isn't it beautiful?' I breathe to Sam.

A grey cloud wisps across the moon's face, then another, racing. And I notice that the tops of trees are whipping back and forth. The wind is high. I can hear it now I listen. It must have been raging all the while Paul and I argued. I can't help thinking of Izzy. If she were here she would make this moon mean something.

'The power-lines must be down,' I tell Sam. 'But the men will mend them soon.'

'Why doesn't the moon go out?' asks Sam.

I touch my son's moonlit hair. 'The moon will never go out,' I say. 'Never. Or not for millions and millions of years. It's not powered by electricity, you see. It's powered by . . .' I look at his moonlit face. '. . . by God.'

'God made everything,' says Sam comfortably. 'He made the earth and the sky and the trees and the flowers and the aeroplanes and the dustbins.'

'Where the hell', comes a shout from the stairs, 'have you put the candles?'

I take Sam back to bed.

'Kate!'

'Coming,' I call.

'Don't go, Mummy.'

'I'm going to get you a candle. A little night-light to have beside you, just until the lights come back on again, OK?'

'No!' He has hold of my hand.

'Tell you what, I'll leave the curtains open and you can see by the light of the moon, till I come up again, OK?'

'Kate!' I hear stumbling against the banister.

'I'm coming!' I call again. 'Can you come and be with Sam for a moment?'

There are some inept footfalls and Paul appears in the doorway.

'Why can you never keep anything tidy!'

'They're in the cupboard under the stairs.'

'Oh, are they!'

'Look at the moon, Dad,' says Sam.

'Lovely,' says Paul, and sits down on the bed with his back to the window.

I feel my way downstairs. I know my steps, my banisters, I feel intimate with my house. Paul has left the door to the stair cupboard open. Without thinking I reach inside and flick the light switch. Fact blindness. I know the lights are out and yet I still try the switch. Or is it just habit? Or hope? I kneel down and locate Paul's tool box, and the box of nails and screws he collects and orders but never uses. Behind them is a shelf of 'my things': a glass ashtray we used to have in the drawing-room in the days when people smoked; some Araldite for the crockery I'd rather glue than throw away; an unopened stick of Iron-kleen, one of Jean's stocking-fillers; a stack of left-over white ceramic tiles and yes, yes, a box of candles. No, two boxes. Prices' stubby, all-purpose household candles. Not the sort you'd have for a dinner party, the sort you'd have for a power-cut. I pull them out and as I do so, I feel a third box. Pumpkin candles! The little slow-burning night-lights Sam and I put in our hollowed-out Hallowe'en faces. I hold my haul to me and negotiate the steps down into the kitchen. The blinds are open and the moon shows me the way to the matches. I light a candle, drip hot wax on to a saucer and have my first lantern. I take two more saucers, a pumpkin light and a second candle and return upstairs. Shadows move on the walls.

'I'm Wee Willie Winkie,' I announce to my son. He's almost asleep.

'Where were they?' asks Paul.

'In the cupboard.'

He huffs, takes the second candle and disappears downstairs.

I clear Sam's bedside stool of toys and set up the night-light. Then I close the curtains and strike a match.

'Pumpkin Man,' I say.

Sam focuses on the tiny bright spot and then yawns and falls into an immediate and deep slumber. The narrowness of the bridge between his waking and sleeping always astonishes me. For a little while I just stand and watch the flicker of light and the rhythmic rise and fall of his chest and then I light my own way downstairs.

In my short absence, Paul has made our house magical. Two candles now burn on the hall table, their flames glowing doubly in the mirror behind. The normally sombre wood of the banisters is burnished red, and the yellow lights of the porch glass are molten gold. The colours and the shadows shift as the flames shift, moving in time with the movement of air, leaning with the weight of what? Of me coming downstairs? I am the disturbance. If Izzy was here – but Izzy is not here. On the kitchen steps is a pale spill of moonlight and on the kitchen table beyond a second collection of candles, bright and dancing, already imbalanced, one candle burning faster, its melt more lopsided than the others. The door to the drawing-room is open and its soft dark lit with three separate flames. One candle burns on the baby-grand, throwing a moon circle on the black piano lid. One burns on the mantelpiece starring the empty, silver candlesticks. The third burns by Paul as he sits in his velvet green chair fiddling with a radio.

'Whole of Brighton's out,' he says as he tunes in the local station.

Half of his face is lit, half shadowed and I think, simultaneously, that he has not forgiven me and that he is wondrously beautiful.

I think also: I am in the wrong.

I am crazy, obsessive, unreasonable. I know this. Know it with my head each time, every time, my heart lashes out. Yet I seem no more able to still my heart than to stop it beating. How easy it was to say to

134

Tessa: you are making yourself unlovable. How difficult to act on my own advice. But I am becoming unlovable. I am driving away the people I love most in the world. Paul. Izzy. I know this. I know it. I will apologize. I will say sorry. Part of me doesn't feel sorry.

'We are lucky to have Sam,' I say.

'The lights are back on in most of Brighton,' says the radio.

'Not here,' says Paul.

We sit in silence for fifteen minutes. Then I think I hear Sam again and get up and go into the hall to listen. The landing light is on. I flick a switch, the hall light comes on. I try the drawing-room. It's on too. In fact, every light in the house is on.

Yet all this while we've been sitting in the dark.

18

The following morning, Friday, Paul readies himself for work. He talks about the riots in Los Angeles, the car needing an MOT, and the possibility that he might join a health club.

'No need to get flabby in middle age,' he says.

He doesn't talk about the row. Sometimes I think each day is totally new for Paul, a fresh start where he can confront (Paul would say 'meet') every person, every situation as if it didn't have a history, reacting calmly, without prejudice. Rationally. Sometimes I suspect he just stores things very deep, screws the lid on them and looks the other way. Then I fear for the day when the lid will, must, blow off. In any case I have missed my opportunity to apologize. The subject is now closed.

Not so with Izzy. She's like me. She'll be brooding. As soon as Paul leaves the house I dial her number. It is really too early to ring but at least I can guarantee finding her in. I know what I'm going to say. I'm going to tell her I had a moment of madness, not unlike the madness during which she conceived. I was obsessed with an idea. I was not practical. Not reasonable. Not kind. I'm going to tell her I'm thrilled with the baby, with her having it, if that's what she wants. I will be the best aunt in the world. My support for her will be total. This is the least she deserves.

'Hello?' Jeff has dragged himself from his bed.

'Sorry to ring so early,' I say. 'Can I speak to Izzy?'

'No,' says Jeff.

'What?'

'She's out.'

'She can't be.' And how would he know? He doesn't normally know if she's alive or dead. 'It's only ten past eight in the morning.'

'Sorry,' says Jeff.

She's avoiding me. She must be.

'Please,' I say.

'Call later,' says Jeff and puts the phone down.

I feel angry, as if he has punched me and I haven't had the opportunity to punch back. Then I think, but I didn't give my name. So maybe it's true, she is out. But then again he could have recognized my voice.

Be calm, bide your time. I get Sam dressed, oversee the cleaning of his teeth and drive him to school. When I return I ring Julia, spin her a line.

'Izzy's had to go back to Oxford. Job opportunity.'

'Oh?'

'Oxford University Press,' I invent.

'Great.'

'Yes, it is great but . . .'

'You need child care.'

'Exactly.'

I have planned this assault meticulously. I talk about the special friendship between our sons, my absolute and particular need for her care, how it would only be temporary (ArtsAid day is less than three weeks away now), how I would pay her, how much I would pay her . . .

'If it helps you out,' she says, 'of course.'

'Thanks, Julia.'

I congratulate myself. Then I read the birth column (three boys, four girls, boy listed first – Adam. God's first-born. This seems like a good sign) and ring Oxford again. It's now 10.15.

'Hello?'

'Hello, who's that?'

'Tony,' says Tony.

Halleluja. I do not know Tony. Ergo Tony does not know me.

'Can I speak to Izzy?'

'I don't think she's in.'

'Would you check for me?'

'Sure.' There is the sound of him calling, walking, pushing doors. Then the sound of voices. Too low for me to distinguish whether he's talking to a man or a woman. After a minute or so he picks up the receiver again.

'Sorry,' he says, 'she is out. Can I take a message?'

'No, thanks.'

'Can I say who called?'

'No. Yes – OK. Susan Waller.'

'Susan Waller,' he repeats, memorizing.

'Bye.'

I put the phone down. Susan Waller was head girl at my school.

Why her? Why the lie? I don't ever remember lying to Izzy before. Not once. Our relationship has always been based on absolute truth, absolute fidelity. I feel a sudden spurt of sickness, as if my world has stopped turning.

At 11.30 they are all out. At least, none of them answers the phone. At twelve I collect Sam from school. He's in hyperactive, cap-flinging mode and I snap at him on the journey home.

'And I won't eat my lunch,' he announces as we park up.

'Then you'll starve to death.'

'I don't care,' he shouts. 'Ner ner ner ner ner!' And then, under his breath, he adds, 'Mum bum.'

'Watch it . . .' I warn, not for the first time.

'Ner ner ner . . .'

'I said watch it!' I steer him roughly through the front door. But I still take care to give him his favourite lunch, bread and cheese and 'grey fish' (a rollmop) – I can do without him interrupting this phone call. As soon as he's settled I go to the drawing-room and dial.

'Hello?' It's Jeff.

'Can I speak to Izzy?'

Jeff sighs and covers the mouthpiece. There is a muffled shout and some mumbling.

'Sorry,' he says, 'she's out.'

'For Christ's sake, Jeff,' I say, 'it's important.'

'Sorry,' he says and puts the phone down.

I ring back immediately. The line cracks with my rage.

'Yes?' It's short, it's sharp and, this time, it's Izzy.

'How do you feel about God?' I ask.

'What?'

'God the father? God the son? God the perfect lover?'

'Jesus the perfect lover,' she says.

'Let you down in spades, didn't He?'

'Are you drunk?' she asks.

'Two teas and a de-caf coff.'

'When I consider thy heavens,' she says, 'the work of thy fingers, the moon and the stars, which thou hast ordained: what is man that thou art mindful of him?'

'But where was He', I ask, 'when you needed Him?'

'Where were you?' she says.

19

Ten days later I'm in Brighton General, the Day Case Unit. I feel like
a day case. It's a Monday. It should have been Friday but they sent a
cyclostyled letter: owing to circumstances, etc.

'What circumstances,' I asked. 'Why?'

'Well, it must mean something,' said Paul, sarcastically.

It means, with recuperation, that I will miss ArtsAid Day. I don't
really care any more. I've done everything the job – and Pippa – have
asked of me this last week and a half. I have worked forty-eight hours a
day, in London, at home, on the phone, till 1 in the morning, working,
working, when all the time I've wanted to be with Izzy.

'Lucky break for Izzy,' says Paul.

And I've done good work, even though my mind has only been half
on the job. The other half's been on Pippa's stomach. I've been
watching it swell, thinking about Izzy. Out of my window everyone
looks pregnant now. Even the men.

'Mrs Francis?'

It's not Izzy's voice, not something she'd say, and it comes from
behind the Day Case Unit desk. But I still look up hoping it will be
Izzy. I quite expected to find her here when we arrived this morning
(Paul and I, though Paul has left now). Izzy does just turn up, knows
when you need her. Knows I need her now. On the day of my
laparoscopy.

'Mrs Francis?' the voice repeats.

'Ms,' I joke.

The woman's white lips purse above her white uniform. She writes
something down. 'Patient deranged', probably. It's not as though I
haven't sent Izzy letters. Well, a letter. A long, special letter, explain-
ing everything. I even apologized without reservation. You can write
things in a letter you can never say even to those people you love most
dearly. I admitted to the madness of jealousy and of grief. I described
my own unloveliness. I asked her to forgive me only in as far as she

loved me, and in as far I love her and always will. God willing. And I talked about the child. I have begun to see this child, dream this child. I know she will be a girl. She will look like Izzy did as a child, as a baby, right down to the pig snout. She will have dark penetrating eyes and a smile of intense innocence. Izzy will love her immediately, passionately, smell her flesh, her hair, fill herself with the newborn bouquet of the child. And I will be first at the hospital. If she will let me, I will be with her, stay with her, throughout the delivery. And I will look at them, mother and child, together, and I will cry, but they won't be painful tears, nor tears of joy, but washing tears at the wonder of them, the awesome circle of mother and child, self-absorbed, complete. Almost so little age between them they could be sisters. And I will feel them both flesh of my flesh and blood of my blood, and I will defend them both like a lioness. All this I have told Izzy.

So why has she said nothing to me?

'Through the white door, please,' says the white uniform.

I imagine my letter lying unregarded on the hall floor along with the junk mail. I see the gentle slide of baked beans from the rubbish sack gradually obliterating Izzy's name on the envelope. Or I think of Izzy taking the letter, holding it, turning it over, but being unable to slide her finger under the flap. I watch her pin the envelope, unopened, on the board by my photo. I see her, after a day or two, turning it to face the wall, stabbing it in the back. But Izzy is quick, observant, unafraid. These images will not do. I know that Izzy has opened and read the letter and has still not responded.

'Hello.' Through the white door is a nurse. 'I'm Gabriel,' he announces deliciously.

'You would be,' I say.

'I beg your pardon?'

I've also apologized about God. Even made a joke of the sort Izzy and I used to find amusing. This whole scenario, I tell her, proves God's not a woman after all. No mother would treat her children like this.

'Come this way,' says Gabriel.

I follow my angel to a bed. There are eight beds in this very white, newly opened ward.

'Sit yourself up.' Beside me on the bed he puts a white hospital gown. 'Backless frock,' he says.

He begins to take notes. His hands are beautiful, his fingers long

140

and masculine, his nails perfectly cut, shaped and buffed. His moons glow. I wonder if his boyfriend is a manicurist.

'Got any worries?' he asks finally, lifting his almond eyes to mine.

'Yes,' I say.

'Oh?' he says, smiling, moving closer. Clearly this is the part of the job he most enjoys.

'I think I left the pressure cooker on.'

'Uh?' He's not sure whether this is a joke.

'It's a joke,' I tell him. His face falls, he looks crushed. 'Sorry,' I say immediately (I say sorry to officials about as often as I say thank you – i.e. a lot), 'it's the nerves.'

'Are you afraid?' He brightens.

'Terrified.'

He reassures me about the anaesthetic, the procedure, the smallness of the resulting hole in my navel. 'It won't even need a stitch,' he beams.

Actually, I'm afraid of them not finding anything. As Paul says, if they find something the size of a pineapple, they can cut it out. And if there is something to be found, then there is an explanation, a reason, a way forward, hope. If they find nothing then there is no reason, no explanation and no hope. I don't tell the Angel Gabriel this.

'Well, if that's OK then, just pop on the gown for me, would you?' He draws the curtains round my bed and I imagine a series of small explosions round the ward as people pop their clothes on and off.

I say 'people' but of course we are all women. This after all is gynaecology. When I'm in my gown and on my bed and the curtains are open once more, I look around. 'Please bring something to read,' said the Day Case instruction leaflet, 'and your glasses and hearing aid.' There are five women on the ward today. Opposite me and to the right a small, dapper, Greek-looking woman with an expensive whiff of perfume, a plummy voice and downcast eyes. Directly opposite is a bony, stillettoed blonde who asks for *Woman's Own*. 'Bet you forgot your hearing aid too, didn't you?' I want to shriek. But I don't. To my left is a fat, mumsy woman in her late thirties and to my right a woman whose age is difficult to gauge on account of her bandages and her burns.

I get out my book but I don't think I'm going to be able to read. Infertility is a great leveller, I'm thinking, when the burns girl announces:

'Christ, they ought never brought me down like this.'

'Where have you come from?' I engage immediately.

'E3,' she declares as if it's both outer space and something I should have known already.

'Is it burns?' I ask inanely. I want to keep the conversation going.

'And grafts. Chooee.' She peels down her sheet and lifts up her hospital gown. There are numerous large gauze bandages. 'They scrape the skin off me thighs and me bum for the other places.' She waves loosely at her breasts, her neck, her face. 'Chooee. It's like being grated.'

'What happened?' I ask.

'Arson.'

'Arson!'

'Yeah. Not to get me. Me boyfriend. They tried done it before.'

'They did?'

'Yeah. Year ago. Came round and stabbed his eyes out.'

'Know anybody by the name of Tessa?' I ask.

'Nah. Who is she?'

'Oh, just someone.'

'My name's Cinth. Hyacinth. Stupid, innit?'

'Kate,' I return.

She flattens the sheet about her grated legs. 'They pushed the stuff through the letter-box. Petrol rags and that. The police said. I never saw nothing but the ball of flame up the stairs. Wall of flame it was.'

'Was your boyfriend bad?' I ask, nodding as tastefully as I can at the bandages.

'Burned bad, you mean?'

'Yuh.'

She laughs. 'He died.'

Behind the *Woman's Own* there's the sound of silent choking. The Greek girl is reading her book but she hasn't turned a page. Mumsy woman is staring, plain and simple. They're all waiting for me to get the next instalment.

'And how do you feel about that,' I ginger.

'Him being dead?'

I nod feebly.

'Better off, I'd say. He weren't no good to no one blind.'

Now I am shocked. I had thought 'stabbed his eyes out' was a figure of speech.

'Aren't you bitter?' I ask, admiring and incredulous.

'Bitter? Nah. What's the point?'

I imagine myself lying under her sheet with her burns and her dead boyfriend. I would be as bitter as acid.

'Why are you here?' I wave at the ward.

142

'I ain't not got a child,' she says, as though I'm faintly imbecile. 'Never took nothing since I was fourteen. Twenny-five next week.' She leans towards me a little. 'I want something all me own. All good like God made. They can't take that away from you, can they?' The yearning in her burnt face is so terrible that I can hardly look at her. But I do look at her, until they come and wheel me away.

'Kate? Kate, can you hear me?'

It's a woman speaking but I wouldn't answer if it was a goat.

'It's all over now, Kate. You're back on the ward. It's finished.'

In my experience nothing's ever finished except the Tampax packet when you get the curse unexpectedly. 'Curse.' The woman at the smear clinic picked me up on that one. 'Why do you call it the curse?' she asked. 'Because it is,' I said. But that wasn't true. I called it the curse because that's what Jean always called it. I'd never questioned it, never even thought about it ' "Curse" is a man's word,' said the Smear Woman. And a biblical word. God's word. Dear God. The only time you don't get the curse is when you have a child. And when you get past childbearing.

'Kate, can you hear me, love?'

I don't call it the curse now. Though it is my curse.

'Kate?'

That and thinking.

'Yes, I hear you.'

'Good girl. Just let me know when you want to sit up and I'll get you tea.'

They wheeled us down in order: Greek, Stiletto, Mumsy, me, Burns. I hear the creak of a trolley. That'll be Burns back, I suppose. Yes, when I open my eyes we're all back. Greek's sitting up, the rest of us are lying white under sheets. There's a hush in the room, of illness, of expectation. Of exam nerves. Have we passed or failed? Who will tell us? In the centre of the ward is a small blue table which wasn't there before. At least I think it wasn't there. It has a pile of notes on it. Our notes. A sister in a belt is working her way methodically through them. She's about fifty-five. Mother hen checking on the breeders who aren't.

'Gabriel?' Mumsy has pulled herself to a sitting position. Gabriel immediately glides over to her and takes her hand.

'Tea?'

'What happened?' Mumsy asks. 'What did they find out?'

He pats her hand. 'Doctor will be round very soon to say.' He nods encouragingly. All of us but Burns, who's still flat out, steal a look at her, willing her to press our case.

'Can't you ...' She's a woman. She's infertile. She can't bring herself quite to ...

Gabriel looks over his shoulder. Sister gets up from the table suddenly and leaves the ward.

'I mean ...' says Mumsy. 'Please?' In the rise of her voice is about seven years of waiting.

'Well,' says Gabriel. 'You're legally entitled now.'

He goes to the table and selects the relevant notes.

In the ward only Burns breathes. She snores.

'Looks like ...' Gabriel lowers his voice confidentially and tells her. There's a pause and then she sinks down without a word. Gabriel looks bemused. I have heard nothing but I imagine he's told her she's clear.

'Gabriel.' Greek and I call him simultaneously. But I am the closest and he comes to me first. Burns begins to stir.

'Please,' I say, 'tell me.'

Obligingly, with one eye on the door, he gets my notes. There is a white form with hieroglyphs on it. It's doctor's scrawl and it's upside down but I'm still reading it: lap and dye, both tubes patent; ovaries normal macroscopic appearance; no evidence of adhesions, no fibroids. No nothing. No fucking nothing.

'You couldn't be more perfect,' says Gabriel.

'Then why!' I scream.

The other women do not look at walls. They look at me. Burns rouses. Stiletto bursts into tears. Mumsy stretches a hand towards me. Our beds are too far apart. She can't reach. Greek shakes and shakes her head.

Then Sister returns. Gabriel quickly shuffles my notes together and proceeds to Burns.

'Hyacinth,' he murmurs, 'are you feeling all right?'

She pulls herself to the upright.

'I didn't have nothink last time, neither,' she says. 'Nor the time before.'

'I'll get tea,' says Gabriel. As he passes the blue table he deposits my notes. Sister continues to write and the hush comes back on the ward.

After about ten minutes Cinth lifts her sheet and her gown and observes her belly.

'Not much to look at, is it?' she says. Beside her other bandages, this square of gauze looks tiny, virginal.

I lift my sheet. My gown is stained crimson, my bandage a welt of blood.

'Christ.'

Cinth looks over. 'Ooh, that's not right.'

I lift the sheet back further, as though that in itself will bring someone to my aid. I look for Gabriel, but he's making tea.

'Call her,' says Cinth, nodding at Sister.

But I don't like to.

'Call her. 'Scuse me . . .' She calls for me.

Sister lays down her weary pen. 'Yes?'

'She's bleedin',' says Cinth.

Sister comes briskly over.

'Hmm,' she says inspecting. 'You'll need a pressure bandage on that.' She constructs one out of three sanitary towels, tapes it on. The blood wells through once more.

'Story of my life,' I say.

'You need a stitch,' she says.

20

Jean arrives at 2.15. You're not allowed to go home unaccompanied and Paul has an unmissable meeting. She brings Sam. She's offered to have us to stay for a couple of days, 'if it helps out'. It will help out — with Sam anyway.

All the other women on the ward have left already except Mumsy, who's in the Day Room. She and I have not been saying much, just feeling close. When she sees Sam her body flexes, tightens. I hope then that Sam will keep quiet, say nothing. After all, Jean could be a child-minder, minding someone else's child.

'Hello, Mum,' says Sam.

I feel I should apologize, but I look in Mumsy's eyes and it's not as simple as that. There is not so much envy as despair. A noise comes out of her mouth, as if someone has stabbed her and she doesn't know where, then she shakes her head, turns to me and — smiles. Such a smile. I put my arms round her, this total stranger, and I kiss her.

'Good luck,' I say.

She nods against me and I feel, but don't hear, the sob.

'I'm parked on a double yellow,' says Jean.

'It smells', says Sam, 'in here.'

I hold Mumsy another moment and then disengage. We don't look at each other again. Sister comes across with my 'post-operative instructions' and thrusts a pot of aspirin and papaveretum pills into my hands.

'Painkillers,' she says.

With these we are apparently free to go. We go.

'Dreadful parking,' says Jean.

Sam takes my hand. 'What did you do in there, Mum?' he asks.

'Saw a man about a baby.'

'What?'

'Never mind,' says Jean.

'The doctors were checking to see if we can have another baby,' I explain at once.

He upturns his face. 'And can we?'

I touch his head, his hair. 'Sure. Yes. They think so.'

'Good,' he says absently.

'They didn't find anything, then,' says Jean at last.

'No.'

She has indeed parked on a double yellow line. And also on the pavement.

'The towaway truck will get you,' says Sam.

We begin the drive in silence, then I realize we are not taking the quickest cross-town route.

'Where are we going?' I ask.

'Cash and Carry.'

'Oh.'

'Only for runny honey. I'm clean out. You don't mind, do you? It'll only take a minute.'

With the detour it will probably take forty-five minutes.

'You're feeling OK, aren't you?'

'Sure.' I have pain in my abdomen, neck and shoulders (that's the gas apparently) and the walk has made me a little woozy. 'Fine.'

At the Cash and Carry, I wait in the car and Sam goes with Jean. I doze a bit and then, when they don't return, read my post-op instructions. I have to stay quietly in bed for two to three days, I mustn't do much housework, cooking or shopping. I must be off work for seven days.

Jean returns with runny honey, Italian tinned tomatoes, tomato purée, apple juice, tin foil, cooking chocolate, Perrier and fresh orange juice.

'Might as well,' she says, 'as we're here.'

'I'm not allowed to do "much shopping",' I say, 'post-operatively speaking.'

'Won't make any difference to you,' she says, 'you never do any shopping anyway.'

It's nearly four o'clock by the time we arrive at Henfield. The phone is ringing as we enter the house. It's Paul.

'Where the hell have you been?' he asks.

'You worried?'

'I wanted to know what happened! What happened?'

'Nothing. Everything's normal. Ovaries. Tubes. Clean bill of health.'

'Marvellous,' he says.

147

I say nothing.

'It is marvellous,' he insists. 'Nothing wrong. I told you.' His voice goes softer, almost dreamy. 'It'll happen, you'll see.'

'Sure. If you say so.'

'I say so.' He also says he'll see me tonight and then he hangs up.

'Bed rest, didn't they say?' says Jean, herding me up the stairs. I'm too tired to resist but not tired enough to sleep. So I lie in bed hating things. I hate the prim, cold feel of this guest room which never has any guests in it. I hate the cheap blue-flowered wallpaper. I hate the sound of my mother fussing round the kitchen and, no doubt, feeding my son sugar titbits. I hate the thought of Paul coming visiting tonight but then going home to sleep at our house, 'because packing up for one night doesn't seem worth it'. Well, it didn't seem worth it when we first discussed it. I resent the fact that my father doesn't come straight up to see me the moment he gets back from the fruit run, even though, when he does come up, we have nothing to say to each other. I hate losing blue dye as well as blood from my vagina. But most of all I hate Izzy who hasn't written and who hasn't rung.

I shake my pills. One or two tablets to be taken every four to six hours when necessary for pain. I take three. They are the size of pound coins and smell like verruca ointment. Perhaps Izzy will ring after six o'clock, cheap rate. But that would be far too planned for her spontaneous self. Besides, she doesn't have a watch.

'How can you live without a watch?' I asked.

'There are plenty of clocks', she says, 'about. If you look. If you need them. And there are the stars.'

At 5.25 the door bell rings. At least I think it's the door bell. The pills have begun to put vacant space in my brain. I pull myself to a vague upright. If it is the door bell, then it's Izzy. It must be.

I hear commotion at the door, an exclamation and some thanks, then the sound of footsteps on the stairs. Jean's.

'Not forgotten, then,' she says, coming in bearing a huge bouquet of pink chrysanthemums and pink carnations, not unlike the bunch I was offered at the hospital.

'It says *Mrs* Francis,' I say, reading the envelope.

'Well, they'd hardly be for me, would they? No one's sent me flowers for forty years!'

'Mrs *J for Jean* Francis.'

'Just open it.'

I open it. In florist's writing, black and shapeless, are the words: 'Thank you for having me, love Izzy.'

I thrust the card at my mother. 'See!' There is a lump rising in my throat.

Jean studies the card. 'Well, she did come here last week, but . . .'

She came to Henfield, she stayed with Jean and she didn't call me.

'For fuck's sake,' I shout, 'look at the card.'

Jean looks. It's a baby congratulations card, a stork with a pink bundle.

'But what . . .'

'It's a joke! A Dorothy Parker joke. Thank you for having me!'

'There's no need to shout, Kate.'

'For Christ's sake.' I sink into my pillows. The lump has turned liquid. I'm going to cry. I'm going to fucking cry.

'She was very peculiar,' muses my mother. 'Very.'

'Oh?' I put my fist across my nose.

'Kept asking why I had her, after so long.'

'And why did you?'

'Because I was pregnant!'

'She must have been a mistake,' I say brutally.

'You were both mistakes,' says Jean.

'Shit.' This hurts. Really hurts. But why? It's not as if I don't know. I look at my mother's absent, uninvolved face. But it's not even that, her lack of care. It's the unfairness of it all. Her conceiving so casually while I am denied. Passion and purpose counting for nothing. God, I hate her. But not as much as I hate God.

'Why didn't you abort?'

'Don't be ridiculous, Kate.' She's unpeeling the cellophane from the flowers. She smells the carnations.

'What's ridiculous about that?'

'One didn't. Not in those days.'

'You mean you would have done if you could have done? If it had been easy?'

She thinks a bit, picks at a petal. 'No,' she says, 'I don't think so. I've liked having you. Really.' She smiles. 'After all, who else would send me flowers? Out of the blue?'

'Out of the pink,' I correct.

'Hmm?' She looks bemused and then, quite suddenly, bored. She shrugs. 'Must go, christening, you know.'

I laugh. What else am I supposed to do?

She takes the flowers, but not the card, and goes. I twist the card in my hand and then I get up and walk along the corridor to my parents' room. It's five past six. There's a phone by the bed and I dial Izzy.

'Hello?' It's Jeff.

'Can I speak to Izzy?'

'No,' says Jeff. 'She's out.'

'Jeff...'

'Really out. And she said she's going to be out tomorrow too. All day.'

'Where? Where's she gone? Where's she going?' I'm turning the card round and round, spinning the pink bundle.

'Don't know.'

But I do. The pink bundle has no face and, all of a sudden, I know.

21

None of them see me leave in the morning. Derek is shaving. He lathers himself with real soap and uses a cut-throat razor which he strops daily on a strip of leather. Sam is riveted, just as I used to be as a child. He wouldn't hear if a stegosaurus passed the bathroom. Jean is more difficult to avoid. She doesn't have a set routine and despite an appearance of absolute disinterest, she has an uncanny knack of knowing precisely who's where in her house. After a couple of false starts, I decide to be blatant.

'I'm going to get a breath of fresh air,' I announce, making for the front door.

'Should you be up?' she wonders to my back.

Probably not. I still have pain in my abdomen and shoulders and I've also been spitting a little blood. I ascribe the blood to the tube they put down your throat and the pain to the fact that I haven't taken any more verruca tablets. I need to be alert for the journey. Jean's car is parked close to the house, not ten feet from the kitchen window. I open the car door, put her key in the ignition and drive out of the gate. Jean, who's in the kitchen, must hear the gravel, but I avoid looking in the rear-view mirror. I've left a note which she'll find soon enough. I've told her when I'll be back, though not where I'm going. I don't want to be pre-empted.

The drive is quick and uneventful, though sitting in one position aggravates the shoulder pain and, after an hour and a half, I feel on the woozy side of tired. It's about fifteen years since I last came this way, but I still remember exactly where Sinclair House is. We used to pass it, as children, on the way to visit Great Aunt Ivy. She was one of my mother's 'duty aunts', which meant (I discovered much later) that Jean hoped to be mentioned in the will. She wasn't, so Izzy and I consumed about two thousand paste sandwiches for nothing. Sinclair House was my, and later Izzy's, final 'are we nearly there?' marker. The building, on the Oxford side of Cuddington, is quite unmistakable. It started life as a school and its main body is Cotswold stone: yellow, warm, comforting. The newer additions are brutish red and stick out like amputated limbs, jammed back on in a hurry. In the centre of the sprawl, in a mock tower, hangs the old school bell. Once, when we were passing on a brisk spring day, the bell rang.

'Bring out your dead,' said my father darkly.

'What is it?' asked Izzy. 'In there?' I think she must have been about four at the time.

'Morgue,' said my father.

'Derek!' said Jean, but made no attempt to enlighten her daughter.

'What's a morgue?' asked Izzy.

'Place for women,' said Derek. My father's not particularly anti-feminist, nor much of a joker, but this remark obviously delighted him. He laughed.

I hear this laugh as I turn into the car-park. There are about twenty-five cars here already. In the spaces marked 'Doctor' there are BMWs, otherwise it's mainly small family saloons. There's one bicycle – not Izzy's. Next to where I park are six skip-sized aluminium bins with blue plastic lids. I wonder what they put in these bins, what they allow themselves to call 'rubbish' here.

I get out and lock the car. There's a sign of the type they have at zoos, left for monkeys, right for tigers, only here it's left for inquiries, right for admissions. Another Sinclair House joke presumably, as all inquiries here are admissions of a sort. I turn right, towards one of the red brick amputations.

Inside, the reception area is dental: clean and hessian with trailing plants, out-of-date magazines and hotel musak. I go at once to the glass reception hatch. There are two clerks, an older woman whose desk faces away from the waiting area and a young mousy-haired girl.

'Good morning,' I say with charm and precision, despite the slightly nauseous swim of my head. 'I'm Kate Francis, Isobel Francis' sister, could you tell me which ward she's in, please?'

Mouse looks at my businesslike face and then at the list in front of her, beginning to trace her finger down the names. But I have already spotted Izzy's. She's in Ward 3, she's listed for 10.45. I look at my watch. It's eleven o'clock.

It's over then. It's finished.

I wait for my reaction – but I don't have one. This is, I imagine, what it's like to be dead.

'Ward 3,' announces Mouse finally. She looks up. 'But I'm sorry, you can't see her now. There's no visiting till six o'clock.'

152

I have prepared myself for many things, but not for this. 'I have to see her,' I say. 'I ... she specifically asked me to come.'

'Sorry,' says the girl.

'She asked me.' I won't be denied. I've come to be here for Izzy and here I'll be. 'She wants me.'

'Nobody's allowed up during theatre. Sorry.' The girl smiles. 'It's the rule.'

'I wonder,' I change tack, 'do you think ...?'

The smile hardens. Mouse into Rat. 'Six till seven,' she says. 'That's visiting hours.'

'Fine.' I must not antagonize her. 'OK. Thanks. I'll come back later then.' Izzy did not show for me, but I will show for her. I spot a drinks dispenser. 'Just get a cup of tea first, if you don't mind.'

'Sure.' Mouse turns back to her typing.

I take my tea to a seat which has a view of everyone and everything in the room. I already have a plan. Relaxed people read magazines. I pick one up. 'I'm not a sex symbol,' screams Raquel Welch. With her for cover I observe the waiting area. There are four women here and one man. The man belongs to a fat eighteen-year-old dressed in black. To look nonchalant he has his feet on an adjacent seat and everyone else is pretending not to have noticed. To my left, beneath a picture of a bluebell wood entitled *Serenity*, is a business-suited woman looking sheepish. To my right there's a girl in a bomber jacket saying 'Wishy Washy' and opposite, a blonde in an incongruous blue boiler suit. Behind me are doors which say 'Office' and 'Staff only', but these look like dead ends. The corridor to the wards must be the one that leads left from the reception hatch. I press my temples, as though I can squeeze away the nag of dizziness. Concentrate. I watch the way the staff criss-cross the room, two nurses and an office worker. Corridor, Staff Only room, reception, corridor again. To get a better look at the corridor, I stand up and move towards an orange poster: 'Don't Trust to Luck. Trust BPAS.' I continue right, poster by poster: 'Sometimes it can help to know you're not alone: Rape Crisis Centre: Someone to talk to? Just Ask. Remember you can ask for counselling whenever you want. It won't cost you any extra.' I pause by the fire alarm. 'Break Glass. Press Here.' One more step. 'A Woman's Guide to Birth Control' with the 'wo' crossed out. There is no one in the corridor, the office worker is in the office, the receptionist is on the phone. I may not have another chance.

I go.

But very slowly, very deliberately. My heart is pounding in my chest. No one calls and I don't look back. Ahead are two trailing bougainvillaeas (silk), a set of five owl prints and three large mirrors, all above waist-height. There is also a notice which says 'Wards 1–3' and an arrow left. The owls watch my walk quicken. There's a noise to my right and, up ahead, the sound of a door opening. Momentarily I freeze, but I have to keep walking, there is nowhere to hide in this corridor. A woman emerges: she's wearing a yellow dress with a white plastic over-apron and she's carrying a bucket. Thank God. I smile broadly, confidently. I nod.

'Morning,' I say and stride past her, left at the arrow.

'Morning,' she mumbles behind me.

Now I'm in a small hall, room to the right of me, room to the left, stairs up, a lift. I hear voices, the grind of the lift, trolley wheels. I must decide, but how? Where is the sign? I wheel about: hall table, pink silk hydrangeas, notice-board: 'All patients, you can see your medical notes, please ask Sister,' vacuum cleaner, spare drip stand, laundry basket, movable blue pay-phone. That's it! The pay-phone. The arrow head is just visible behind it. I'm about to push the phone aside when the door on my right opens. I flatten myself against the wall. A nurse steers out a patient in a wheelchair. The only place they can go and not see me is the lift. They go to the lift, backs towards me. The nurse presses the call button. After the door opens I will have about thirty seconds before the nurse goes in, turns round, selects the floor number and stares me straight in the face. And that's if no one comes out of the lift in the first place. I wait, wait, wait – wait for the shove and clunk of the lift's arrival, and then, under the clatter of gates, move the phone. Ward 3 is right. There is only one right, the room from which the nurse exited. I flail into it, waiting for the shout behind me. There is nothing. The shout in front? Nothing. I resume breathing, look about me. The ward is empty.

Quietly I return to the door and almost close it. Now no one can take me unawares. Then I check for the basin – far corner right. I may be going to be sick. Keep calm. Perhaps she's in the recovery room and the nurse will bring her back when she's delivered the new patient? Delivered. I swallow hard to keep down the rise of acid.

There are six beds in this ward but only two are occupied, Izzy's and, presumably, the wheelchair woman's. On the table beside Izzy's bed is a jug of water and her Latin American handbag. It is the only splash of colour in this white, white room. The sheets are white, the bedcovers white, the bedsteads white, the walls white, the bins white, the silk flowers (azaleas) white, the visitors' chairs white (with black seats), the lampshades white (with thin gold trim), even the television is white. The roses on the dividing curtains are not white, they're

154

pink, but they are so delicate, so washed, that they look white. In fact everything is so clean, so prim, so tastefully white that the room seems to be making a statement, or rather a denial, restrained, polite: 'You see? Nothing nasty ever happens in here. Be reasonable.'

Be reasonable!

This is a room to shed blood in. To make crimson. I go to Izzy's cupboard and finger her things: her glasses, her address book, a virgin tablet of Lily of the Valley soap, some loose change, a hairbrush, her Sony Walkman. I take the Walkman and partially draw Izzy's curtain, not so far that a nurse would notice, but far enough to conceal me from the door. I sit behind it, on the wheelchair woman's side, and put in the ear-plugs. There is a tape already in the machine and I press 'play'. It's Pachelbel's Canon. At once my head spumes with nausea, torrents with the sounds of the Madrid flautist. Around me the air bursts with iridescent bubbles. I feel an expectation, a yearning, and I reach, reach for the child. But there is no child. Only the music sobbing and the sudden slip of blood. The blood might be running down the inside of my skull or down the walls of this white white room. I think it is on the walls, womb walls. And it's not a drip, it's a gush, a spill, flowing with the music, red running, running red, again and again, da capo, da capo. Life leaking. And then come the cries, the screams. The yelps of the newborn, the howls of each child who would have been born, should have been born but for this white white room. They cry in their thousands, perhaps in their millions, and they are comfortless for they are to cry as long as the music cries, which is for ever. Da capo.

Then I hear another sound, against the blood, beneath the screams, the low pulse of a woman sobbing. And I think it must be me and I rock with the sobs until I hear a voice saying, 'Why are you crying so much?'

They have wheeled Izzy back into the ward. Her face is running tears. She is blind to the nurse who speaks to her and plumps her pillows.

'It's all over now,' says the nurse. 'It's finished.' She pats Izzy's hand. 'It's not that bad. Really. It's just the anaesthetic. It takes some people this way. You'll feel better when you've had tea. You'll see.' She smiles and wheels away with the chair.

I lay the music aside and pull the curtain. Izzy sees me, but not before my arms are around her neck. I hold her crushingly close, so that there is nothing in the room but her.

And despite the screams and the blood, I say, 'You did right. Izzy it's all right. You were right.'

155

'I was wrong,' she screams. 'Wrong! Wrong! Wrong!'
And she pushes me so hard that I fall to the floor.

22

'You stupid bitch.'

It's my husband talking. I can hear him, though not see him. I have my eyes closed. Last time I opened my eyes I was sick and they pummelled me and shouted at me and stuck a needle in my thigh. Even Izzy said, 'Leave her alone.'

'You stupid, stupid bitch.' He's stroking my hand.

They've put me to bed. I can feel the starched, antiseptic sheets and the hard hospital mattress. I can smell the white of the walls. But it's not Izzy's ward. I think it's a single room, I think I was screaming. My head feels as though it has been flung a far distance; I concentrate on trying to gather it to me. My eyelids glow yellow-red. Electric light. That, and Paul, mean I must have slept a long time. Outside it will be dark. I open my eyes.

'How's Izzy?'

'Christ.' Paul throws down my hand. 'Can't you think of anyone but your sister?'

I look up at the ceiling. I should have said, 'Hi.'

'Hi,' I say and I try a smile on him.

'What sort of a stupid fucking stunt did you think you were pulling anyway?'

'It wasn't a stunt.'

'Oh, wasn't it – driving two hundred miles the day after a general anaesthetic? What would you call it, a suicide bid?'

'It's only ninety miles,' I mumble, but of course he's not listening.

'How can you be so irresponsible? If you can't think of yourself, perhaps you could think of your son for once, or even your husband! You're a wife now. You're a mother. We should be your first family. Your first responsibility.'

'Izzy needed me.'

'And Sam didn't? What do you think he felt like to be abandoned without a word and then have his Gran do her nut in the kitchen?'

157

'She probably only missed the car. And Derek's got a car.'

'She did not miss the car. She was worried about you. She was out of her mind about you.'

'I left her a note.'

'Bravo. Halleluja. But you didn't say where you were going, did you? And you weren't supposed to be driving anyway. She called me at the office.'

'Oh.'

'I thought you were dead.'

'OK,' I say. 'I'm sorry.'

He sits down, calms down, kisses me on the forehead. 'You stupid bitch.' There's a pause, then he says, 'Do you know how long it took me to get here? Nearly five hours.'

'Five hours?'

'Because I had to come on the sodding train, didn't I? Else we'd have two cars here, wouldn't we?'

I want to laugh but I don't.

'I'm not having it again, Kate,' he says, suddenly serious. 'This is the absolutely last time you put Izzy before us. Before yourself.'

'Or else.'

'Yes. Or else.' He looks me hard in the eyes. 'How do you feel?'

'Pretty rotten.'

'Good. I'm glad. You deserve to.' He gets up again and drums his fingers on my bedside table. 'The only good thing about this whole affair is that at least Izzy's made the right decision.'

'She doesn't think so.' I pause. 'Paul, don't be angry with me, but is she OK? Is she?'

'I wouldn't know. She's discharged herself.'

'Discharged herself?'

'Yes, that's what I said. Stayed long enough to give the nurses your name and address and then just walked out. Didn't even wait to see if you were OK.'

'Oh.' The hurt beats in my chest. 'She was very distressed.'

'If you ask me, she was very selfish. So what's new.'

'Don't . . .' I say.

'And don't you!' he exclaims. 'Don't you defend her any more.'

I shut up then. I feel suddenly utterly exhausted, as though I will never again have the stomach to fight. 'Can I go home?' I ask. 'Can we go home?'

'I don't know,' says Paul. 'I'll have to check.'

He goes out of the room and returns with a nurse.

'This is Sister,' he says. 'Sister.' He almosts laughs.

Sister shakes her head, prods me and asks the inevitable questions: how do I feel, have I got a headache, do I have visual disturbance, what do I remember? Then she takes my temperature, checks my blood pressure and shines a light in my eyes.

'You could really have done yourself a damage,' she says.

This time Paul does laugh.

'Doctor will be round in a minute,' she then tells Paul, over my head. 'I'll get him to come and have a quick look.'

The minute is about three-quarters of an hour but the doctor is nice, tolerant and faintly amused. He says I'm fine and if I stay fine for an hour, I can go.

'So long as you've got someone to take you.' He looks at Paul. 'Be responsible for you during the next twenty-four hours or so.'

'I drew the short straw,' says Paul. 'I got to be responsible for life.'

We sign some papers.

'If they charge us, it's coming out of your wages,' says Paul.

'Fine. Stop my pocket money. See if I care.'

In an hour I'm judged fit, so we go. We don't talk much during the journey. I doze and Paul listens to music. At the junction in Henfield, we take the turn towards my mother's house.

'I thought you said you'd take me home,' I say.

'Your son's at his Grandma's,' says Paul. 'Did you forget?'

'No.'

'And even though someone well enough to drive to Oxford is probably well enough to look after their own son in their own house, you're just going to stay at Jean's for the next few days. And when I say stay, I mean stay. And I'm staying too. Nights, anyway.'

'Got a ball and chain?'

'No. But I'll be taking your shoes.'

As we crunch into the drive, I realize that I haven't the stamina to face Jean.

'I'm really tired,' I tell Paul. 'Could you just clear it for me to go straight upstairs, without, you know, seeing anyone?'

'Sure.'

He opens the door, fields me to the stairs and then makes a barrier of himself at the kitchen door. It's nearly ten to ten. I walk along the landing to Sam's room and tuck him up. I kiss his head, half hoping he'll wake, but of course he doesn't. Then I slip into my parents' room, lift the phone and dial.

'Hello,' says Tony.

'Is she OK? Is Izzy OK?'

'Yup. She's fine.'

159

'Can I speak to her?'

'No, I'm afraid she's staying over with a friend tonight. A girlfriend.'

'Who?'

'Beth. Beth Stanwick.'

'Can I have her number?'

'It's a squat. They're not on the phone.'

'Tony . . .'

'And Kate, she's going away tomorrow. Abroad, I think.'

'What the hell are you doing!' Paul has caught me. I drop the phone.

'She's going abroad,' I tell him.

'Leave it!' he shouts. 'For Christ's sake, Kate, leave it!'

When I wake in the morning Paul is gone. I am aware of his absence even before I come to full consciousness, just as I always know when he comes to bed, even if I am asleep.

This is our marriage.

I stretch my hand into his space. It's cold. Perhaps I have slept very late, drugged, exhausted. I pull myself up and fumble for the switch on Jean's guest-room light. It's one of those old-fashioned switches, a tuberous growth on the flex. I begin to feel slightly uneasy, it's too dark in the room and the house still seems to have its night hush. There is no Sam and Sam always arrives before 6.30. Can it be earlier than this? Finally I locate the switch and ingite the lamp. It's 5.55. Paul never gets up this early. Never.

I panic, even though I know he may be in the bathroom. But the space is too cold for the bathroom, he's too long gone. Besides he never uses the bathroom in the night, has a bladder like a camel. I try to be reasonable, to be rational. The only rational explanation is that my husband has left me. That I finally drove him to the edge and he jumped over. We rowed after the phone call last night. He shouted, 'That's it! I've had it with you!' Later, much later, he came to bed. I heard him, no felt him. Did I feel him? He kissed me. But I wasn't awake and he was. He couldn't sleep. He tossed and turned, played the day back in his mind, brooded. This won't do. Paul never broods. But maybe last night he did. Or maybe the man who never snaps, who'll love me for ever, maybe he snapped. I'm talking to myself in Jean's spare room, talking to fill the void, because suddenly here it is, a huge black space with me suspended in the middle of it. And just for a moment all of my love for Paul comes crowding in on me and with it fear and grief, as if he's dead. As if I know what I cannot know, that I will never see him again, never be with him again. And the loss is so unsupportable that I cry out, 'Paul!'

'Do you want to wake the whole house?' Paul comes into the room.

'What the hell are you doing?' I cry.

'What does it look like I'm doing? I'm getting up. I'm getting dressed. I'm having breakfast. Correction, have had breakfast.'

'But it's not six o'clock!'

'Good. Because I have to be in Cambridge at nine.'

'Why?'

'To see Dr Simon Stubbs, eminent medievalist and illuminated manuscript bore.'

'You never arrange meetings at nine.'

'And I didn't arrange this one. I rearranged it, or rather my assistant did. From 3 p.m. yesterday afternoon.' He pauses. 'Any idea where I was at 3 p.m. yesterday?'

I watch him move around the room, pull drawers out of the spare room chest.

'I'm going to be better, Paul,' I say.

'And I haven't even got any clean socks.'

'I'm going to make it up to you. Going to put you first.'

He opens the spare-room wardrobe, rifles through the mothballed blankets. 'Or any pants. Didn't get to go home last night, you see.'

'I love you.'

He shuts the wardrobe door and comes over to the bed. 'It's a long time since you said that.'

'For a moment I thought ... when you weren't here ...'

He kisses me. 'You couldn't creep into your parents' room and borrow some of Derek's underwear, could you?'

'Sure.' I get out of bed. On the front of my night-dress is a crimson stain.

Paul looks at it and then at me. 'And another thing you're going to do, is get that stitch seen to.'

'Sure.'

Forty-five minutes later, Paul's gone. He's wearing a pair of Derek's white bloomers, some criss-cross patterned socks (the only navy pair I could find in the dark) and yesterday's crumpled suit. He is not in a good mood.

Jean is not in a good mood either.

'I'm so glad you're here now,' says Sam.

'That makes one of you,' says Jean.

She's partly taking it out on me directly (mainly for the inconsideration of not letting her know where I was going) and partly making me Izzy's whipping boy.

'You'd have thought she could have told her own mother!'

'She did tell you.' I defend my sister. 'In her way. When she sent those flowers. When she thanked you for not aborting her.'

Jean, who has been pacing, sits down hard at the kitchen table and puts her head in her hands. A small, spare woman, she suddenly looks not much more than a child herself, bony and bereft.

'Is she all right?' Jean asks.

'No,' I say.

'Why did she do it?'

'Which bit of it?'

'The abortion. Why did she have the abortion? I'd have had the child. If it was a problem.'

'You!' I am aghast. 'You don't even have time for Sam!'

'I don't have to have time for Sam. You have time for Sam. But if I'd taken responsibility, we'd have managed, Derek and I. Arranged things. It could have been done. Might even have been nice, after all these years.'

Now she looks old, and rather brave and wan. I wonder what I look like? How does someone who's shocked and angry and whose heart is somersaulting look? I admire my mother because I think it's true, she would have taken the child in her abrupt, unemotional way, just got on with it, made time and never remarked upon it again. I am also jealous and piqued because this sudden, solid solicitude does not, as ever, seem to include me. She hasn't once inquired how I am, or asked me to talk about the way I feel. And the possibility that I might have wanted the child or cared for the child or been passionate about the child, or even thought about the child at all, none of this seems to have crossed her mind. She doesn't care and that makes me hollow. But feeling hollow is self-pitying. Selfish. And that's not allowable, so I end up feeling guilty. Sit in a pile of guilt, a mire of guilt. A mountain. Is it just me?

'I tried to call her this morning,' says my mother.

'You did?'

'She wasn't in.'

'Tell me about it.'

'They say she's going abroad. Abroad! What does she want to go abroad for?'

'Get away from us all. That's what Paul says.'

Absently, Jean picks up the salt cellar and begins to grind a pile of sea salt. 'Maybe he's right. Some things are better left unsaid.'

162

There's a pause, a grind and then she bangs down the salt cellar like a full stop. 'Shouldn't you be getting Sam dressed for school?' she says. And that's the end of it.

For her.

Derek takes his grandson to school. The only thing my father has said to me today is 'Good morning,' and I expect it took him most of the night to perfect that. I wonder for a moment how my parents managed to convey their love for each other. It can't be verbal. I just can't hear either of them actually saying it, the big 'I love you.' (Just as I can't hear them, in my childhood memory, saying 'I love you' to me. Or to Izzy.) As I search the phone book for my GP's number, I imagine them as two blocks of stone, which have rubbed so close for so long that they have just eroded into the shape of each other, their love silent, slab-like, monumental.

Later, as one of the slabs slips on her yellow rubber washing-up gloves, I say, 'I've managed to get a 3 p.m. appointment with Dr Viney. Get my stitch looked at.'

'Is it giving you bother?'

'Well, it's just not doing a very good job of holding my belly together.'

'Fine,' she says. 'Derek can drop you on the lard and flour run.'

He does – and I'm grateful for small mercies. Basics is one thing my father can get enthusiastic about; their abundance, packaging, relative price, the amount you save bulk-buying. So I'm glad to be dropped pre-Cash and Carry, to sit in the waiting-room, waiting. It would hurt me today to find him loquacious about lard.

'Kate Francis,' the receptionist calls, and hands me my battered notes. I knock on Dr Viney's door and go straight in, without waiting for an answer. He sits facing a wall and has to turn sideways when patients come in.

'Hello,' he grins, 'what can I do for you today?'

Every time I come here Dr Viney looks younger. Maybe I'm just getting older, or maybe it's because he's ginger-haired and the ginger-haired seem to have immunity from the ageing process. Ten years ago he looked about thirty-five. He still looks about thirty-five. It would be better, for today's purposes, if he were older.

'I think I'm going bonkers,' I inform him. I feel embarrassed about this as it's only a five-minute appointment and he's already running twenty-five minutes late.

'Oh?' says Dr Viney.

'My sister got pregnant,' I elaborate, 'and I belted her. Then she had an abortion and she belted me. Then my husband got up early this

163

morning and I thought he was dead. And my nanny tried to commit suicide and my mother doesn't give a shit. About anything. Especially me.' I fix him with a glassy stare. 'So how come I want to be the mother in spades?'

'Hmm,' says Dr Viney, a little bemusedly, flipping back through my notes for a reference point.

'But the real thing is lack of control. I thought I could control my life and I can't. So I thought I should be like my sister and not try. Relax a bit. But she's not so *che sarà sarà* after all, because what did she do with her spontaneous baby? Abort it, that's what. Do you see what I mean?'

'Mm,' says the doctor.

'And I met a woman in hospital who had third-degree burns and whose boyfriend was dead and who had no child at all and I thought I should be grateful. But I wasn't. That's the problem with other people's lives, isn't it? They don't touch you as they should.'

Dr Viney keeps his head down and his counsel to himself.

'So while I do think I should relax more,' I conclude, 'I also think it's important for me to remain in control, or, in this case, resume control. So, if I'm not pregnant in three months, could you refer me to a shrink, please?'

'Certainly,' says Dr Viney with alacrity.

After that he looks at my stitch. When he takes off the bandage the wound is, for the first time, bloodlessly clean.

'Looks OK to me,' he says.

'Story of my life,' I say, and he nods and laughs as if he understands, which he doesn't, of course.

But I don't mind because I'm feeling very positive. Paul's going this morning really frightened me and I meant what I said, I am going to change. Admitting the problem to Dr Viney, and setting a deadline for the shrink, this is the first step. I've also decided not to take the drugs this month or the herbs. Not even the swimming-pool tea. I'm going to make peace with my body and call a truce with my brain. I'm going to be better.

I really am.

23

On Sunday it's ArtsAid Day. It makes the main evening news, Channel 4 anyway. They interview Pippa standing on the roof of the Festival Hall. It's from here that twenty thousand red balloons are to be released, each one carrying an arts quote, each one a potential raffle ticket. If you find one of the tags ('Great art is as irrational as great music. It is mad with its own loveliness,' George Jean Nathan, *House of Satan*, or 'It's clever but is it art?' Kipling, *The Conundrum of the Workshops*), then you fill in your name and address, send a donation to ArtsAid and stand to win one of numerous glittering arts prizes: an original oil painting by Howard Hodgkin (donated by the artist); a pair of Madonna's stage shoes (white satin and rather grubby); a box at Covent Garden for *Don Giovanni*; a year's free film pass to the Ritzi Cinema; £250 of music from Virgin Records; £250 of books from Waterstones. It's a brilliant idea and it was mine. I don't think Pippa, in her enthusiasm (and she has that flushed everything-is-going-marvellously look), mentions this fact. But it's not exactly at the top of my mental agenda either. What I'm thinking about as I watch her pink animation and her very short skirt is that, unbeknownst to the camera, she is now almost fifteen weeks pregnant. This means she's not being sick any more. It also means that it is highly unlikely that she will miscarry.

'I'm jealous,' I say.

Jean lifts her head from the devils-on-horseback (we are of course in the kitchen), squints at the television and says, 'What is she wearing?'

'The good news', I say, 'is that she'll soon be wearing a tent.'

Sam also squints at Pippa.

'Where's Josh?' he asks with that delightful women-as-mother-only tunnel vision with which all children seem to be born.

'At home with his Dad,' replies Paul morosely, as if he's doing the work himself. Tonight we will be going home. This, I think, will improve Paul's temper.

'Any tea?' Derek clomps into the kitchen unaware that anything which touches my life is on the television.

But does it touch my life? It should do. I've put in enough work and it's obviously going extremely well and it's all in a very good cause. I should be proud. Pippa is clearly exhilarated. Would I be exhilarated if I were there, with the camera on my face and the South Bank wind in my hair? Maybe. Momentarily. Just now I feel joyless – despite my best intentions, my new resolutions. There's a kind of depression that defeats the brain. I experience it physically, wave after wave of it. It comes quite suddenly, moving through me, emptying me out, so that, for a moment, I feel there is nothing inside me at all. It rarely comes on cue, as now. I can be thinking about supper, or Sam, about the lack of loo-rolls or the night sky. It passes, of course. All things pass.

The camera angle changes, revealing the sponsor, Samuel Jackson, the Chairman of the Big Red Balloon Company, and Kylie Minogue. It fixes on Kylie. Flashing a smile as sharp as her scissors, Kylie cuts the red ribbon which fastens the net of balloons. There's a float and a jump and then a sudden cheer from the fans on the ground below and bridge above. The red balloons leap, they stream into the air, thousands and thousands of them. Kylie leans forward in delight and shakes the net to make them move faster, each one lifting and flying. The crowd roar, every face upturned; to Kylie, to the balloons, to the heavens.

And I look up too. In my November sky are twenty thousand wombs. Each one empty.

24

It's Advent. Sam's school have constructed a candelabra out of coathangers. At its corners, four red candles perch in four painted bits of egg-box.

'When they're all burnt down,' says Sam, 'then it's Christmas.'

'If the school hasn't burnt down first,' I say.

There has been tinsel in the shops for three weeks, the fruiterers have dates nestling among the tangerines and the men who sell foil wrapping paper at ten pence a sheet have set up their stalls in Churchill Square. The shops are in green and gold *flagrante* and even the weather has begun to pinch. Father Christmas rides in white lights down Western Road, the charity workers are rattling their tins and Sam's Advent calendar has so far yielded a bauble, a dwarf, a snowman, a bell, a reindeer, a Christmas tree and a pile of presents. Each morning we both try to guess what item will be behind the glittery door. Despite Sam's attempts to cheat, we have been consistently wrong.

'I know what that one is,' says Sam, pointing at number 24.

'Oh?'

'It's the Baby Jesus,' he says, with confident glee. 'And Mary and Joseph and the donkey.'

That's another thing I hold against God – immaculate conception. No waiting around for Ms Mary. It'll be Friday next week, said the Angel Gabriel. Put it in your diary. Oh, the luxury of certainty! To be able to organize your life, make a five-year schedule. Sometimes I think it's just this – the uncertainty of non-conception – which is so crushing. The not knowing when, if ever. A state of limbo where planning is an impossibility because all the important decisions depend on 'x' and 'x' is unknowable. Mind you, knowing didn't seem to help our Mary. She still managed to wind up in a stable for the birth.

I'm trying to be jolly. I know how the suicide rate climbs over the festive period. Besides, I owe it to Sam, to Paul. I did, after all, promise. The Christmas cards don't help, though. I send about a hundred and twenty – each year more resentfully. The easy ones to write, the ones to friends you saw just last week in which you scrawl, 'Love Kate and Paul and Sam', seem utterly pointless; the ones requiring a little more work, those to old friends with whom you're really out of touch, are merely sentimental; and the only really useful ones, to good friends who happen to live abroad and to whom you'd like to write more often anyway, those are the ones you miss the deadline for. Of course, you don't realize you've missed the deadline until their card arrives on 15 December by which time you can't even make it back with a New Year greeting. And that's leaving guilt out of it.

I complain. I protest. I ask Paul why he never writes Christmas cards, even to his old school friends, who have somehow become my responsibility over the years.

Paul shrugs. 'Don't bother with them. No one will notice.'

I'm sure he's right. But, in my habitual way, I keep bothering. Besides, I like receiving Christmas cards. I like the certainty (here I go again) of mail on the mat, the heaviness of the thud. Or I did. Now I get up every morning and look for a letter from Izzy. I scrabble through the envelopes, searching for her familiar hand, scanning for a foreign postmark. Jeff says she's gone to France. Tony says she's gone to France. But where would she stay? What would she do? She has no job. She has no money. She doesn't speak French. Not very well, anyway.

'She'll meet people,' says Paul. 'She'll busk.'

'It's very inconsiderate', says Jean, 'not letting us know where she is.'

'She'll be twenty-one', says Derek, 'soon.'

Twenty-one on 7 December, a Saturday. Jean and I think she may call home, may even come home. It would be like her, we say, to turn up unexpectedly.

'I'm going to buy her a gun,' says Sam.

'Bags I supply the bullets,' says Paul.

We agree to congregate at my parents' house, leaving a note pinned to my Brighton door: 'Hi Izz – come to Henfield!'

'You're all mad,' says Derek, expressing an opinion.

On the day itself, at 10.30, Jean says, 'I shall bake a cake. She'll never come this morning. She never gets up in the morning.'

She bakes – with Sam beside her as chief spatula sucker – a bizarre tangerine and chocolate confection.

168

'Izzy really liked this cake', she defends herself, 'when she was a child.'

I watch her fold the orange gloop with a wooden spoon. I'm less surprised by the cake, which I don't remember as a favourite, than by my mother's apparent sentimentality. She scrapes the mix into two large round tins and sets it in the oven where it rises and goldens and perfumes the house.

'Yum,' says Sam.

When it has cooled on its wire rack, Jean sandwiches the layers together with chocolate butter icing. Then she kneads orange colouring into a block of royal icing and rolls it paper thin.

'I don't know why I'm doing this,' she says, dropping the icing over the cake and folding carefully it down. 'In the old days I just flung on some tinned tangerine segments.' Five minutes later the cake is on the decorating stand. 'Happy Birthday, darling Izzy, 21 today', Jean writes in molten chocolate.

'You didn't write "Darling" on my twenty-first cake,' I remark.

'I gave you a party,' says Jean.

Sam is allowed to stick twenty-one silver candles into twenty-one orange candle holders and to glue on (with icing) a silver key with a white ribbon threaded through it.

'Just happened to have them in stock,' says Jean.

Derek snorts. He's watching his wife spin the stand and web the cake edges with more molten chocolate, lines so fine that they harden almost before they touch the cake surface.

We are all listening for the door bell, for the return of the prodigal. Jean sets the finished cake in the middle of the kitchen table and we wait. Paul reads a paper. The rest of us fidget. At two o'clock the roast scheduled for a late lunch, 'just in case', can wait in the slow oven no longer. We sit down and eat. Then the phone rings.

'Aha,' says Jean, triumphantly, and goes into the hall. Forks remain poised, salt-pots suspended.

'Oh,' says Jean, 'Maureen.'

But she returns smiling. 'Second helpings?' she says.

Paul has a second helping.

'That was Maureen,' Jean says after a while.

'Grief,' says Paul, but I think only I hear it.

Lunch continues, it drags, punctuated by Sam chopping at his plate. He doesn't like roast lamb, or broccoli, or sprouts or even roast potatoes.

'You can't get down', says Jean, 'until you've eaten something.'

I cut up the potato and mix it with redcurrant jelly for my son.

'Eat that,' I say and I pray.

He eats it. Maybe there is a God after all.

After lunch, Sam says, 'Can we go out now?'

'No,' says Jean.

'It's too cold.' I say.

It is cold and unpleasant; a freezing drizzle spatters against the window-panes.

'I'm hot,' says Sam.

'I'm suffocating,' says Paul.

But we all stay in.

'Do you think I might open a window?' says Paul.

'Why not,' says Jean.

Paul slides up a sash and the chill is immediate. Nobody says anything. The rain beats into the silence of the house.

'Is it tea yet?' asks Sam for the seventeenth time.

At nearly six o'clock it's tea.

'Yeah,' says Sam. 'Can we have the cake now, Gran?'

'Frankly,' said Derek, looking at his wife, 'I don't see why not.'

'No,' says Jean.

'But...'

'I said no.'

By seven o'clock a tearful Sam has dug a finger through the icing, broken off a piece of chocolate web and been roundly reproved.

At 11 p.m. Jean says, 'Sod it,' and scrapes the cake straight into the bin.

We go shopping, Sam and I. He's a tall boy for his age, about elbow height, handbag height. He does not have a good time. Nobody in Brighton seems to know that there is a recession on, and the pavements are five deep with people and bags and buggies. The large shops are crowded, the small ones impassable. Everyone is harassed and avoiding eye-contact. Sam is bored, impatient and twitchy – just like his father is when shopping. I think it's hormonal. We force our way out of the fug of Marks and Spencers (regulation food parcel for aged aunt) and on to the milling street.

'Keep hold of my hand.'

'You said that,' Sam growls, tugging my arm and twisting a shopping bag tighter about my wrist. 'About a hundred times.'

I negotiate him to the kerb and we cross between a standstill of buses.

'Look!' Sam wants to stop mid-road and admire the Odeon bus which swarms with super-heroes.

'It's Batman,' he cries with the first enthusiasm of the afternoon, 'and Spiderman and the Joker and Daredevil. Look!'

'Come on, Sam.'

We have to queue to get on to the pavement the other side as there are railings and, behind them, the foil-paper stallholder is doing brisk and bottleneck business. We are almost through, and in sight of the doors of W.H.Smith's (crackers), when a disembodied voice yells, 'Sam!'

Sam jerks me backwards and I drop the carrier which contains the red serviettes, the gold spray paint (hydrangea heads and fir-cones), the Pritt glue and the four tubes of glitter. I'm on my knees immediately but it's already too late. The green tube has been stamped on.

'Hi,' says Tessa.

Sam looks at me and then at the pavement. Around his motionless feet the glitter blows.

I stand up.

'Hello,' I say.

'Han't he grown!' Tessa marvels. Her face is flushed and exuberant and she's mountainous with presents.

'You think?'

'And look at his hair!' she laughs.

I look, but I don't see the joke.

'It's so long! Like a girl!'

'S'not,' says Sam to his trainers.

'I've got something for you.' Tessa sloughs off her crinkling baggage. 'Was gonna bring it up.' She scrumples and searches, oblivious of the glares of the passers-by, or at least of those people who are attempting to pass by the mound she has made at her feet. Sam is now giving her his rapt attention.

'Shouldn't we move?' I gesture feebly at the slightly less congested corner of the building.

'For Christ's sake!' A middle-aged man deliberately swings a Debenham's bag at Tessa's rear end.

'Piss off,' she says seasonally and without looking up. 'Here!' She pulls a huge box out of a huge Tesco's bag. It's wrapped in snowman paper and has an elaborate snowman tag of the sort that I won't buy because they're so expensive. She thrusts the box into Sam's more than willing hands. He looks up at me with a mixture of longing, innocence and despair.

'Go on,' Tessa says, 'open it now.' And she begins ripping off the paper. Sam, whose face registers greed and disbelief in equal measure, does not need any encouragement. At once the mood around us changes from irritation to indignation and the whines of the other small children increase in pitch.

'Shut up!' yells one mother for all of us.

'What is it?' says Sam, scrabbling furiously. 'What is it!'

'It's a tank,' says a delighted Tessa, before the toy is even half revealed. 'It's great. It's amazing. You wait!'

But they can't wait, least of all Tessa. She pulls at the box-flap and extracts a green and black, battery-operated monstrosity.

'Look! Look!' She sets it down on the pavement and flicks a switch. At once it spits into life, the turret whirling and the red and yellow gun mouth flashing and rack-tack-tacking indiscriminately.

Sam is awe-struck.

'He loves it! Don' 'e, don' 'e!' she sing-songs rapturously.

'Say thank you, Sam,' I manage.

Sam is kneeling covetously close to the machine, absorbing its splendours and the envious gazes of the boys around him.

'I love it,' he says.

'Told you,' says Tessa.

'Thank you very much,' I say to her. 'You shouldn't have done. It looks far too much money.'

'S'all right,' she says. 'It's great, innit Sam? Look!' She pulls a second switch and the caterpillar treads start moving. I think of the books I've bought Sam and the jigsaws, and the new paints. And, luckily, the Batman suit.

I also think what an extraordinary person Tessa is.

'What are you doing now?' I ask her.

'Working in a café,' she says. 'Piss money.' She grins.

'And Rosemary?'

She lets go a peel of laughter. 'Oh, I've moved on.'

And that, I realize, is precisely it. Tessa has moved on. Her bruises have healed, her suicide bid is just a memory, one passionate relationship is over and another one probably begun. She has progressed, survived, moved on. Can this be true? Has she really vanquished the pain, so that she can go to bed and sleep dreamlessly? I fast-forward her life and arrive on her death-bed. Has she really nothing to regret? I don't know.

What I do know is that she's crouching on the pavement full of joy. I watch her play with Sam, heedless of everything about her. A sudden gust of wind showers her with glitter. The sparkle in her bottle-blonde hair is green.

On Thursday, 12th December it's Sam's Nativity Play. It's his first school play and I find myself unexpectedly excited. Sam is more cold-blooded. He wanted to be Joseph and he's the second king. I always wanted to be Mary and I was always the second king too.

Sam sits on the stage in a purple table-cloth. In his hands he holds a vase covered in silver foil which he periodically up-ends and inspects. The children are all sitting on benches, shiny-eyed and fidgety as they wait to sing or to be called forward as their parts demand. I wish Paul could have been here, but he's at the University of Kent. Other fathers are here, well over half of them. There are also a dozen cameras and three or four videocams. They are grasped in the hands of parents avid to record this tiny rite of passage. I don't have a camera because I don't want to experience this through glass. I want to feel it as it happens, watch it unfold raw against me and then conjure it again in my memory.

The teacher, Mrs Watkins, calls the class to order and they begin. At once we are enchanted. Whatever the children were doing we would be enchanted. As it happens, Mary and Joseph are leading Thomas Saunders round on all fours. He's playing the donkey and swishing his fat woollen tail. Sam is now sitting straight-backed on the bench, motionless, serious. For of course, whatever and wherever the action is, I mainly look at my son – until they sing 'Away in a Manger', that is. We have arrived at the stable and Mary sits on a stool with Joseph standing behind her. His right arm is on her shoulder, protective, masculine and, in Ross Bunburry's case, twitching. Mrs Watkins, at the piano, nods exaggeratedly and strikes the first chords of the carol. The children, with varying degrees of swiftness, open their mouths and sing. The sound they make is ragged, tuneless and absolutely heart-breaking. I'm not sure exactly what is so moving about it; maybe the sound alone, maybe the collective innocence of these unsullied singing souls, or their unselfconsciousness, or the fact that I suddenly feel swept by the preciousness of childhood and its unrecoverability. There are tears in my throat even before I hear the wail behind me. It's the jerking, demanding cry of a very tiny baby, almost newborn. On stage Mary looks vaguely down into the shoebox full of straw in front of her and, as if suddenly remembering herself, reaches down for the infant Jesus, lifts him up and cuddles him to her. The baby in the audience quietens. I blow my nose.

'Dreadful, isn't it?' coos Mrs Bunburry into my right ear. 'Bless 'em.' And, despite Mrs Watkins' warnings about flash cameras and children's concentration, the parental paparazzi click and snap and whirr.

When the show is over and the ecstatic applause dies away, Thomas Saunders' mother jumps up and presents Mrs Watkins with a bouquet of pink carnations and a small package wrapped in glittery paper.

'To say thank you from all of us,' she laughs in her nervous and excited way, though I for one knew nothing of the gift. But then Mrs Saunders is a full-time mother. She has time for her son, time for Mrs Watkins, time for detail and generosity. Or she's made time, chosen childhood. I look and look at Sam – searching myself.

'The children can go home in their costumes,' announces Mrs Watkins. 'And thank you. Thank you all so very much.' She's grey-haired and rather moved.

I walk back home with my king. He has his duffle coat over his cloak which nevertheless streams out purple behind him. He trots and skips in his lanky, inexpert way.

'Did you like it?' he sings. 'Did you?'

'I loved it.'

He squats down suddenly and gathers a handful of gravel which he tips into his silvered vase. Then he stands up and rattles his treasure.

'When we have our new baby,' he announces, 'I'll get it some frankincense.'

When I open the door to our house, there is just one letter on the mat, a white triangular-flapped envelope lying face down.

'Is it for me?' chants Sam.

'No.' I know this even before I pick the envelope up and turn it over.

'Ohhh,' he complains.

'Tell you what,' I say, 'as a special treat, why don't you have lunch in the playroom with Sesame Street?' I am afraid that this one time he will refuse; I hold the envelope and my breath.

'OK.' He skips into the playroom and abandons his duffle coat on the sofa.

I can hardly bear to let the envelope leave my hand, but I force myself to put it down, propped up where I can see it as I make Sam's quick salami and cheese lunch. The postmark is Edinburgh.

'Here.' I hand Sam his plate.

'Can I have a drink?'

It seems to take more time to make a Ribena than it would to create the world, but I have to do it, Sam must be content to be quiet.

174

'Thanks, Mum.' His eyes are glued to the screen.

'Just going to the loo,' I announce. I went to the loo to read my O level results. And my A level results. I close the lid of the toilet and sit down. But I don't open the letter, I just stare at it: at Izzy's handwriting, its slope, the blackness of her biro. I observe the stamp (first class), check the date (yesterday's – 11 December) and once again the postmark. Edinburgh. Edinburgh – the bitch!

And then it starts – the swell and lurch of all the emotions I have been swallowing down, a sudden, noxious vomit of anger and grief, guilt and despair. But it's the anger which comes first and seems most bitter. Anger at the casualness of Izzy's conception and the casualness with which she disposed of her child. Anger against her – and against God – for the unfairness of it all. The abitrariness. The stupidity. The waste. Anger as passionate as my love for her, carved and scored against my heart for the time she pushed me away when I came to comfort her in hospital, despite what it cost me and what she must have known it would cost me. And anger of course against myself. For I should never have asked for the child. What's given freely is a blessing and what's demanded a curse. And she could have given, being so specially Izzy, so much my beloved sister, given something I myself could never have given. For it seems impossible to me that a woman who has held her own child in her arms, even for but a moment, could possibly ever lift that child towards someone else, no matter the depth of their love. And that I should ask her to be so much the un-mother fills me with a horror and a self-loathing that she herself will only know when she does at last hold a child in her arms. And I blame myself also for the loss of her and for the tangerine cake which went in the bin. And my grief at her going from me, physically, emotionally, is as sharp as the knife I have turned against her and as hollow as Paul's absence from me the morning I woke without him. I think perhaps God punishes me for so hurting my always child, my Izzy. And I think also, how have I so lidded and controlled these emotions which now spew in the downstairs toilet? Perhaps, my seventeen years with Paul have not been wasted after all.

I open the letter.

My dearest Kate

I'm sitting on the Crags, high above the city. A volcanic outcrop, an eruption of stone. Basalt, I think. I can't believe it was ever hot, liquid. It's so cold now. Everything's so cold. It's not snowing but it might as well be. I haven't brought gloves and I have ice instead of bones in my fingers. Maybe you think I have ice in my heart too,

Kate? If you love me enough to think I still have a heart.

How can you feel the loss of something – someone – you never saw, never touched, never knew? But I did know her, Kate. You were right. It would have been a girl. They scraped everything out of me that day except that, the knowledge. All my insides, my emotions, my right to be. I thought about killing myself. I know it sounds melodramatic, but I did. Do you know what stopped me? You. I thought you'd be angry. Hope you're having a good laugh at that.

When I was a child I often used to think of myself as an orphan. Derek wasn't really my father. Well, he isn't really a father, is he? He's a sort of space. Do you know, I don't have one childhood memory of him playing with me? I know we have photos of him and me on the beach, but I don't remember it. Not one time. And as for a mother, if I had one it was you. Though I don't suppose that's escaped you. So where does that leave Jean? I was going over and over it in my mind, because I just don't feel like a daughter to her, or that she loved me like a mother should. Whatever that means. And then it was my birthday. And I wanted so much to speak to you but I couldn't, do you know why? Because I realized it wasn't *my* birthday at all. But her birthday. Do you see what I mean? We think we own our birthdays. But we don't. They are the days on which our mothers gave birth. And I thought about my baby. And I thought at least my mother loved me enough to give birth to me. So I'm twenty-one and already a worse mother than Jean. And do you know who I want to comfort me about that, Kate? You.

And if you think that's confused, try this. Why did I do it? I can hardly bring myself to write the word 'abort'. It's against everything I hold most dear in the world. Against God (no particular order here, Kate), and spontaneity and response and love and loving-kindness and chaos and beauty and the sanctity of all things. And against you, Kate. I tried to blame you, at first. That you pushed me, that I couldn't keep the child and you, Kate. Couldn't hold my child and look in your childless eye. And so I chose you. That's what I told myself at first. There is no truth. I think that more and more. Certainly that wasn't true. I think I really was too afraid. Too conventional. Too selfish. Wanted too much my own life. I thought there would be another time right for a child but not now, not this time. And I forgot, made myself forget, that it wouldn't be the same child next time. That I killed a child. They never say that at the clinics, you know. At the clinics they do terminations. They tell you about hormones in the clinics. They say, 'Your hormones may go bonkers for a couple of days.' They tell you to take aspirin.

I'm sorry I didn't stay in the hospital for you, Kate, I couldn't face you because I couldn't face myself. That is the truth.

Why don't they tell you about the loss? I dream about the knife and I hear the scraping. Feel it. Sometimes I dream the more they scrape, the bigger I become and the more empty. And I hear this song, a tape I took into the clinic, Pachelbel's Canon. Do you know it? It da capos and I dream it too, hollowing out my head as the knife hollows my womb. I say 'my womb' but it feels like my heart. And when I look at the blood – and I'm still bleeding, Kate, and it's nearly a month – I think it's my heart's blood.

Helen says I should see a doctor. She's the girl I'm staying with. I lied about France, as I guess you've guessed. Helen's got a five-month-old daughter called Aurora. I look after her when Helen goes to college. It's not as weird as it sounds – a joy as well as a penance.

I miss you, Kate. I feel you may not love me. May never be able to love me again. And I feel that loss too, every day. I feel if I'd been bigger, or braver or stronger or more lovely you would have your child. I feel I could not have loved you enough, yet I don't know how to love you more. Teach me, Kate.

Ever and always your sister, I.

There is no address at the top of this letter. I hug the pages to me and go upstairs to the bathroom. I need Tampax. I have begun to bleed.

25

On Christmas Eve, Paul and I always have a small party. We do light, festive food – smoked salmon sandwiches, stilton and apples, clementines, mince pies and cream – and invite our best friends. Pippa and Richard come, Christian and his boyfriend Nick, and each year, Izzy. At 11.25, Izzy draws me away from my guests and out into the night. We go to Midnight Mass together. Izzy because she loves God and me – why do I go? From sentiment, I suppose, and a little spirituality and a sense of drama and a need to assuage and locate. And for the delight of being out on a starlit night with my sister. There are always stars on Christmas Eve night. Always were. There is no Izzy tonight.

The party has been warm nonetheless. I think this drawing-room of ours must have been made for Christmas. Paul has lit both the front and the back fires and each grate glows with an orange contentment, quietly illuminating the white throats of the deco lilies which climb the surrounding tiles. Around each mantel are strings of tiny Victorian red-glass beads which I have wound into garlands with holly from the Downs and decorated with fir-cones sprayed gold by Sam. Hanging from each of the central lights is one of Sam's new flour-and-water-paste creations. At the front end of the room a red fire engine threaded up with purple string. At the back a lopsided green and glittering Christmas tree. They wink darkly at us in the candle flames, for we have no electric lights on tonight.

It's just past eleven o'clock – that velvet time of a winter's night. Nick is sitting at the piano, joy on his sprite dark face. He's a small, agile man whose body is never in complete repose, like a city which never sleeps. He's been playing for over an hour now, his light fingers touching out carols, mooning movie songs, improvising, singing and calling out to us to sing. Christian, who hasn't much of a voice, is sitting on the sofa, eating thick dark chocolates from Audrey's. As he bites into a green mint centre, he looks up at Nick, not for the first time this last hour. There is nothing but gladness and admiration in his eyes, and this I love about him so much, how he relishes Nick's talent and enjoys the way he is, despite himself, the centre of attention.

Pippa is sitting next to Christian, her hand on her belly. She's twenty weeks pregnant now and it shows on her small, bony body. She's wearing black stockings, a short black skirt which rises over the bulge, a silk camisole and a floaty see-through black shirt, buttoned at the wrists and laced at the throat. She's also wearing jewels, huge papier-mâché gold and red crowns in her ears and a red and gold and blue sceptre pinned to her breast. The glass of champagne beside her is hardly touched but her eyes are shining. She looks at her belly and at Richard and at the garlanded mantel and sighs. Despite her arty dress and the sharp remarks that issue occasionally from her mouth, she is beginning to look cow-like.

Richard is sitting on what Sam called the 'dragon chair' – a carved and upright chair with a leviathan lashing at its back and sea-serpents for arms. It's a big chair but he's bigger, and comfortable in it. He looks quite different from the way he did that day at the beach. He's the old Richard, relaxed, confident, mandated. Penguin apparently love the first six chapters of his book and there's the prospect of a foreign editor's job in the offing too.

'All fell into place when the child-care did,' he says, happily, smiling at me. Smiling at Pippa.

'Talking of child-care,' Christian says, looking at Pippa's belly, 'what's going to happen to ArtsAid now?'

'It'll go on,' says Pippa, from her sofa recline. 'It's big business, you know. We made over a million quid. Maybe a million and a half.'

'But what about,' Christian nods at the bulge, 'you know, the baby?'

'It'll cope,' says Pippa, grimly. Then, seeing Christian's slightly aggrieved, politically correct face, 'Just need some bright spark to cover me for a few weeks.'

'A few months,' interjects Richard. 'Six, preferably.'

Pippa laughs.

'Mind you, they're queuing up to employ her now,' Richard continues. 'Four charities head-hunting last week alone.'

'Nobody called me,' I say.

'You weren't a media star,' sings Nick from the piano.

Pippa sits up a little. 'Would you want to have been called?' she asks. 'Would you want to work for any outfit other than ours?'

I think about this. 'It's always nice to be wanted. But no, I don't think I'd want to work for anyone but us. Perhaps, in fact, I'd want to work more for us?' I'm testing a theory: what do people with only one child do to make their lives important, significant? Love their work more? Their friends?

I get up, cross to the sofa and kiss Christian on the head.

'What's that for?' he asks.

'For Christmas. For mending my leak. For nothing in particular.'

'A kiss is just a kiss . . .' lilts Nick.

'And one for the media star.' I kiss the cow.

'Bags I in,' says Richard and gets a kiss on the neck.

'And me,' says Nick. When I go to the piano he takes his hands from the keys and puts his arms around me.

'You're gorgeous,' he says and kisses me on the mouth.

Then I look for Paul. But he's out in the kitchen brewing another jug of fresh coffee.

It's then that the door bell rings.

'Who the hell . . .' Paul appears with the brimming cafetière.

'Santa Claus,' says Christian.

'Didn't want to get his feet burnt,' says Nick.

'Carol singers,' offers Pippa.

'I'll go.' I'm already half-way down the hall. We have a spy-hole in our door, but I don't look through it, can't bear to be disappointed. I wrench open the door. Outside is a small, windswept figure with a rucksack half on and half off her shoulders. Izzy.

'I'm sorry,' she says, 'I should have called. Let you know I was coming. You won't have any food.'

'Izzy.' I take her in my arms and hold her as if the world was about to end.

And she holds me. Her head is on my shoulder, my hands are in her hair. I feel the gulping rise of her chest against me. 'I love you. You stupid bitch. Love you.'

This is how, some minutes later, Paul finds us.

'Izzy,' he says, 'hi.'

She breaks the clasp.

'Hi, Paul.'

'Let me take that.' He lifts her rucksack and she knows she's welcomed in. She looks at her watch and then at me. It's 11.25.

'Is it OK?' I ask Paul.

'Of course.' He's smiling. He's such a very good man.

Izzy and I leave for Midnight Mass.

We, who always talk, say nothing. I feel as if I've been given a very precious gift and I can't say thank you adequately. We walk to the Seven Dials beneath a cold and cloudless sky. There are stars —

millions upon millions of them. We climb up the hill towards St Nicholas'.

'There are very few people', says Izzy, 'with whom silence is companionable.'

And, as I look at her smile, I think, there will be time, there is no hurry. She is not going away again. Wait. Breathe her. And I breathe in the cold starlit air.

The brow of the hill is high above Brighton. It feels as if one could see the sea, but somehow the sky seems to mass right over the town and the view is the view of the night.

We begin the slight descent towards the church. There are other people now, old ladies with sticks and furs, smartly dressed party-goers with laughter and alcohol on their lips, families with teenage sons in ill-fitting suits, a nun, some single men. We join the flow towards the Mother of All Brighton Churches. I have not seen this sign before. It's pinned to the church gate. The Mother is square-towered and made of grey flint. She's powerful, immutable, but also strangely welcoming, rough-hewn, not too big, the hand of man as well as God upon her. The path to the front door is red brick, earthy and immediate.

We go in, Izzy and I. Already the pews are packed, the people gay, expectant, murmuring. Izzy scans the church and then leads the way down the side aisle to a vacant pew on the right, quite close to the altar. As we kneel the organ strikes for Emmanuel and the service begins.

We are celebrating the birth of a child.

I join in. I sing and I look at the oil painting which hangs before me. It depicts the Holy Family, Mary and Joseph, heads together, close over their son's crib. They have the ordinary look of parents, absorbed in their child, awed by the miracle of him and yet simultaneously intimate with him. The light that illumines their bowed faces comes from the infant himself. And I think – yes, it is so. Then the readings begin and I hear the words of wonder, comforting and mythic in their familiarity. The high, painted altar screen flickers in the light of eight candles. I trace the pattern of roses that join the pairs of angels. The flowers are embossed silver, their brilliance faded now. The stems which twine them together are nature's green but the thorns, which are sharp and many, these are blood red. This also, I think, is so. At prayers my eyes rest upon the Christmas tree. It is a tall, gangly affair with too little tinsel thrown haphazardly about it. The baubles are also inadequate and the lights, such as they are, only brighten half its branches. I love this tree because it seems so specially human. It is the time to pray for forgiveness. They don't give you very long to list

list your sins but then maybe I have more sins than most. And I, who don't believe in God, ask Him to forgive me for those things I have done unto Izzy and unto Paul and unto Sam. And those things I have not done.

I also ask Him for a child.

Then I eat bread and drink wine and look at the people. Coming to the communion rail, slowly, unable to pick their feet from the ground, are four thin men. They lift their hollowed faces to the cross but do not kneel before it. Perhaps they would not be able to rise again. They are Aids victims and I think, they will not see another Christmas. They are humbling in their dignity and though I know they have walked many miles beyond me, I still take the liberty of offering a prayer for them and, in doing so, I also remember Cinth who was burned and her boyfriend who was killed. Then I pray for Tessa who probably doesn't need my prayers, and for Jean because she's my mother, and for Derek so as not to leave him out. By this time we are singing again.

The pairs of angels hold shields between them. The left shield is painted with a hammer and a pair of pliers, the right one is too dark to distinguish and the top one depicts nails. Nails with which to build or to hammer through a human hand. Carved into the wood which arches behind the altar are grapes. Grapes to make wine and wrath. I don't know whether it's because I'm standing so close to Izzy that there suddenly seems a balance and purity to life after all. I reach out my hand and I touch her, this most beloved sister of mine who I might have lost, who I deserved to lose, but who is now close beside me, singing with a voice so beautiful she might herself be an angel of God. 'Yea Lord, we greet thee,' she sings, 'born this happy morning.' And if I feel close to tears they are tears of gratefulness and of joy. And I sing too – as if my lungs would burst.

'Go in peace,' declares the Reverend and the organ fanfares our release back into the world. Izzy and I rise as one person and move together towards the little rack for candles. We post our ten pences and take a candle each. Izzy lights hers first and I light mine from hers. We both bow our heads briefly and then queue to leave.

'Happy Christmas,' says the Reverend, 'oh happy, happy Christmas.'

Out in the starlit night, I say, 'Was it for the baby?'

'No,' Izzy smiles, 'it was for you.'

I wait for her to ask me about my candle. But she doesn't, afraid perhaps that mine was for a child. But it wasn't.

'It was for you,' I tell her.

Then we walk up the brick path and up the hill embraced by the night.

At the Dials I say, 'I feel sorry for the vicar, though. It must be very depressing to have your church packed to overflowing and know that none of them are coming back next Sunday.'

'Oh no,' Izzy says at once. 'I wouldn't feel like that at all if I were the vicar. I'd think, what an opportunity. What a chance to seed something in the hearts of all these people, something so important it will last for a year.'

Her exuberance makes her grow and I think suddenly, and with a mother's tenderness, it is all right then, she has survived, she will survive. Move on. Then I remember her singing and I think, no, she will not move on, she will fly – and I must not look where she's flying to, just be glad. And I am glad.

We have arrived at our door. Paul greets us. In our absence the others have left and Paul has cleared away. He has also hung three stockings from the mantelpiece, one for Sam and one for me and one for Izzy. I have not appreciated this man enough.

'Brandy?' He brings us glasses of amber fire. 'Happy Christmas,' he says. Later I discover he has also made up a bed for Izzy.

It's half-past two by the time we get upstairs.

'Thank you,' I say to my husband, my lover.

And that night we don't fuck. We make love.

26

'There,' says Derek, bringing in the crib on a silver tray.

It's five o'clock, Christmas tea time. We are sitting in my parents' back parlour, a room that escaped the expansion of the kitchen only by virtue of being the wrong side of the stairs. It is normally a cold and cheerless place, but Jean has brightened it with a fake Christmas tree and, suspended from the ceiling, a number of huge purple glass baubles. They're Victorian and have a rich, reflective and, in the context of this room, rather crass appeal.

'It's totally edible,' Derek adds, and he beams, proud and a little shy. To make the stable he has rolled out sheets of chocolate and iced them into thatch. He has constructed two marzipan shepherds, a flock of white chocolate sheep, three conical kings with cochineal lips and cherries for crowns and a marzipan Mary and Joseph with icing smiles. Jesus, on a bed of yellow sugar strands, is wrapped in rice paper and has a white chocolate button for a halo. Above them hangs the Angel Gabriel, an ethereal confection of spun sugar.

'All except the star, that is.' He waves at the foil star from which an unlit sparkler protrudes.

'Yikey crikey,' says Sam, rising from his just unwrapped fort and coming to inspect this new wonder.

'It's instead of a cake,' Derek says, setting the tray down on the low coffee table. 'Because ... you know ...' He glances up at Jean.

'Didn't want another one to go in the bin,' says my mother.

This is the first allusion to Izzy and her unannounced return. Immediately I'm alert for rancour, but Jean's tone is strictly matter-of-fact. It was the same this morning when Izzy was handed her presents, some in Christmas paper and some in birthday paper. Nothing was said, almost nothing was implied. And certainly nothing was asked. This silent reabsorption of Izzy might have struck me previously as insensitive, censorious in a way that Izzy could not combat because, since no explanation was sought from her, she had no opportunity to mitigate, to defend. But looking at them both, Derek bent over the crib and Jean watching him from the sofa, I think, no, their reaction is quite genuine, accepting, even kind. Whatever their faults, they are not sulking people, grudging people, and if I admired Paul for his welcome of Izzy last night, his gentle, silent enfolding, then I must admire my parents too.

'I'm sorry for being so out of touch,' says Izzy, suddenly, as if she knew about the cake, which of course she couldn't.

'Doesn't matter,' says Jean.

'You're an adult,' says Derek, quietly. 'You have your own life to lead.'

Then I remember that Jean didn't abort Izzy and she didn't abort me and I get up and kiss her.

'Good grief,' she says. 'What's that for?'

'Mistletoe.'

She looks heavenwards. 'What mistletoe?'

'Things don't always have to be for things,' says Izzy. 'Sometimes they can just – be.'

'Oh,' says Jean.

'It's for all the times I didn't kiss you,' I say. 'When I might have done.' I want to kiss my father too but I don't know how, so I hover clumsily and then sit down. I never kiss him now, not even a peck of greeting. I remember Izzy's words: 'He's not a father, he's a sort of space.' Yet here he is, a kind old grandfatherish man, who has taken the time to create something totally magical for his grandson. And the time is Christmas – a busy, profitable time for caterers. Then I realize that, in all the years, he and Jean have never once taken an order which would have meant not spending Christmas Day with us. 'To be delivered on Christmas Eve' – how often have I heard him say that, or seen it written, or watched him race around the countryside, so everything should be delivered, finished by midnight, 24 December. Have I noticed this, been grateful, said thank you?

'Thank you, Dad,' I say. The 'Dad' is difficult on my tongue and he looks up, surprised. 'It's amazing. The crib.'

I suppose I've always been waiting for him to make the effort, but why should it be his responsibility? He's not an articulate man and opening conversations of any sort just doesn't come naturally to him. I am good at talk, pride myself on it. I should talk. What would I say? I've never heard him express any enthusiasm for anything other than the business and the garden, and the garden's mainly business anyhow.

185

'It must have taken you hours,' I say. Now he smiles, vague and rather pleased with himself.

Do I love him? I want to love him so much, or perhaps I just want him to love me? What is this obsession of mine with love, with being loved? As if I'm somehow starved of love – which I'm not. I look at my husband. He's still wearing his cocky green cracker hat and his always beautiful mouth appears, as usual, to be smiling. I love him, there is no doubt about this. It's not something I have to think about at all. My reaction is immediate, automatic. Perhaps too automatic. Perhaps I need to learn to love him again, show my love. This has not been an easy year for him. Euphemism. I have made it hard for him, because I found it hard myself.

'Can you eat the hay?' asks Sam.

'Not yet you can't,' says Grandad and he reaches into his pocket. 'Oh blow!' He stalks back into the kitchen mumbling, 'Matches.' Sam follows him like a dog and there is a momentary silence. Izzy takes the poker and gives the fire a desultory prod.

'Let me do that,' says Jean. This room is used so infrequently that Derek rarely builds a fire and his effort today is sparse and dying. 'Are you going to go back to Edinburgh?' Jean asks suddenly from her knees, looking at the coal-glove and not at her daughter.

'I'm going to get a job. Or I'm going to try to.' Izzy speaks quickly, glancing at me and at her mother's back, and I think, she's seeking approval, wanting, despite herself, to do right by us.

'I thought you had a job,' says Paul. 'Looking after whats-her-name's child?'

'Helen only really needed me while her Mum was off having a hysterotomy.'

'Oh – so what'll you do?'

'Don't know.' Her gaze is just on me now. 'Unless Kate gives me a job – while Pippa's on maternity leave.'

There's something in her eyes I don't understand, an intensity, an appeal, so that while my heart cries, 'Yes! Yes! Give her the job, have her with you, teach her, give to her,' I just stare at her, saying nothing.

'Don't be too enthusiastic,' says Paul.

Then it all falls into place and I say, 'No. Sorry, Izz. It's just not your cup of tea.'

'Kate!' says Jean.

But Izzy is smiling as if someone has just cut the rope from about her neck.

'You've got different talents, have to do your own thing.' And I feel a release too, but it's not me who's flying but Izzy – like a bird, like an angel.

'What talents?' says Jean.

Derek sticks his head round the door. 'Would you believe we're out of matches?'

'No,' says Jean curtly. 'Second drawer down, sink two.'

'But I also have to organize a little more,' says Izzy. 'Plan things. Can't always expect the good things just to bump into me.'

'Can hope though,' I say. 'Can be alert. Respond.' My sister's face is radiant. 'Can I have your gift for responding, Izzy?'

'Sure. It's yours.' And she begins to laugh. Then I laugh too, uncontrollably.

'Why can't you two grow up?' says Jean. Then we laugh some more because of course it's not that easy. Jean stares at us with her old, baffled look. 'It's like that vest,' she declares suddenly. 'The vest . . .'

'With the rose!' shrieks Izzy.

'When you were eighteen months old.'

'And now I'm twenty-one! I've come-of-age.'

Then there are tears in both our eyes, not for the vest of course but for the impossibility of ever really coming-of-age.

'And Kate's thirty-five!' wails Izzy. Then she shakes her head because she knows and I know that all you can do is keep on trying. And we're both going to try – hard. After all, we both have blood on our hands.

'Here we go then.' Derek is back, rattling a large box of Cook's matches. 'Now just watch this.' He sets Sam in front of the nativity scene and lights the sparkler. It glows red for a moment and then it fizzes into life, throwing star after star into the stable sky. The spun sugar angel pirouettes in the breeze, his white wings suddenly iridescent.

Sam stands perfectly still, his eyes on the rain of stars and the gyrating angel. The lock of his body brings Paul from the fireplace. I feel my husband's hand slip into mine and together we move around Sam, so as to be able to see the whole of his face. His smile is rapturous and amazed and he is so captivated by this moment I don't think he would notice if the earth cracked in two. Paul squeezes my hand and I know that the delight which is mine is his also. And in this second I think, can there really be anything more than this? The hand of your beloved in your hand and the joy of watching your child grow? Can one expect, can one deserve more than this? It should be enough. I will respond and make it enough.

Then the sparkler gutters and Sam says, 'Can I eat Jesus?'

187

Seven days later I bleed. Not blood that anyone else would notice. Not really even blood at all, just as much pink mucus as would colour the tip of your little finger. But it's the beginning, as it always is, of my period which will start in earnest one week hence. The pink turns cerise, the cerise crimson and the crimson blackens into blood.

I also have pain, in my stomach and in my head. This is the end of the second month since the laparoscopy, the second of my three opportunities to beat chance. I go upstairs to the bathroom and search for the paracetamol. The foil packet is half empty. I press out the remaining pills and swallow each of them down, four of them, one at a time with a glass of water. The last one sticks in my throat and I gag a little. As I rinse the toothmug, I look out of the bathroom window. It's a beautiful day, cold and brilliantly blue, with a sun so pale it's almost white. There are no clouds now, but there will be, snow is forecast for the weekend.

I put away the toothmug. I hope it will snow. I hope also, despite the pink and the pain, that I will not get my period. It is 1 January, the first day of a new year, a time of beginnings, of resolution, of hope. Of dreams. I shut the bathroom cabinet and look at myself in the mirror.

What is a world without dreams?

27

It doesn't snow, not at the weekend, not the following week. The skies are greyer though, lowering, heavy with promise. Sam sits at the kitchen window, waiting. In the hall his brand new plastic sledge gleams drily. Next birthday he will be four. It hasn't snowed since he was born.

'Is this it?' he cries when it finally begins to rain.

'No,' I say, shattering illusions.

It's twenty-eight days now and I haven't got my period. I'm not late, but late for me. Since Sam's birth I've had one cycle of twenty-nine days and all the rest have been shorter: twenty-four, twenty-six, twenty-three, twenty-one. I have a record of every single month. My average cycle is twenty-three days. But what's average? What do statistics matter?

Every night I go to bed and pray I won't have blood in the morning (the spots of pink are still just spots) and every night I rise at 3 a.m. or 4 a.m. and test. I wake then because Sam wakes. Paul thinks his room is too cold and he rouses when his body temperature drops. Yet when we tried the thicker duvet on him, he woke drenched in sweat, his hair matted to his scalp.

'You're wrong,' I say. 'It can't be that.'

'Then why?' says Paul. 'He hasn't woken since he was ten months old.'

I shrug and watch and wait. On Day 29 he wakes at 4.30 a.m. He cries but does not leave his bed so I go to him.

'What is it?' I say.

'I had a dream,' he weeps.

'What dream?'

But he shakes his head, he doesn't know. His eyes close with tears still wet on the lashes. I notice the curtain is open a little and get up to nip it shut.

'Don't do that,' says Sam, his back towards me. 'I want to be able to see when it snows.'

'So do I,' I say and fling the curtains wide.

I don't use a pregnancy test. Not that night. If I'm negative – when I'm negative – that's the end of hope. So I just use my finger and leave the curtains open.

On 9 January, Day 30, I wake at 5 a.m. The house seems silent but I know Sam must have cried out, so I slip out of bed and cross the landing to his room. There is a tiny fluttering snore as Sam turns in his sleep. I touch his head, checking, and he moans lightly. Reassured, I tuck him up, securing his duvet with a sheet. Then I look out of the window. It's snowing – a silent powder-fall in the blackness. I watch the tiny spiralling flakes float down to earth. They're too scant and insubstantial to settle, they're melting on the grass. Immediately I want to shake Sam awake, in case this is all of the snow we shall have, so he will at least have seen it. But then I remember his question to me at bedtime: 'It will snow, won't it, Mummy?' And my reply, emphatic, definite, responding to his need: 'Yes.'

'Enough for a snowball?'

'Yes.'

'For a snowman?'

'Yes.'

So I keep faith and I keep quiet. I hope. The pregnancy test is in among the pants in my chest of drawers. With Clear Blue there are two testers in each kit. There's only one left now, the other one I gave to Izzy. I go to the bathroom and pull off the plastic lid, revealing the absorbent dipstick. I feel a lurch – fear, I think. Then I sit on the toilet and piss. The noise of splashing is the only noise in the silent house. I pull the stick from the stream and replace the lid. Already as I finish and rise from the toilet, the urine is climbing, up, up, to the first window where the appearance of the blue line signifies that the test is working. It's working.

And now I wait, the few seconds more before the urine reaches the second, higher window. Window of opportunity. Window of destiny. Opening of hell. Eye of the storm. Eye of snow. Just ten seconds. Maybe thirty seconds. A lifetime. A child's life. There seems to be something, something faint. A mirage. My brain playing tricks. The faintest of lines, just a darker edge, maybe just wetness, but turning bluer, not really blue. Yes, blue. Yes, a line. A blue line. *A blue line*.

I'm pregnant.

I want to scream, I want to cry, I hear my breathing, my heart. It's not true. It's a lie. I look again. I don't believe it. I don't fucking believe it. I'm down on my knees, my head on the bath. There's a song in my skull, a pop song, 'I fall on my knees and pray', it's going round and round and my ears are buzzing as if someone else is doing the singing, the talking, the thinking. 'Thank you, God, don't take it away. Please don't take it away. I don't believe it. Thank you.'

After a minuteless time I rise to my feet and I dream out of the bathroom, up the steps and along the corridor to our bedroom. I take the test with me, my certificate, my proof. My talisman. Will the line fade by morning? If it does, how will I know again, how be sure? I'm not sure, I look again. The baby will be born in September. The baby. Such a difficult word to say even to myself alone in the dark. I'm not alone, I have Paul, sleeping soundly beside me. I want to wake him but of course I don't. What would I say? I might miscarry. I'll probably miscarry. That would be par for the course. It's 5.30. I can't sleep, won't sleep again tonight. I get up again and creep downstairs. The blinds aren't drawn in the kitchen and snow is swirling against the window-panes. It seems thicker, it is thicker. The grass is slightly white. I'll make myself a cup of coffee. No, I'm pregnant, I'll make tea. Less caffeine. Has it got less caffeine? Have to check. I boil the kettle. It's cold this time of the night, the morning. I light all four gas rings to give me some heat.

I am so happy.

Sam will be four and a half, an unremarkable age-gap. I am going to open my front door and dance in the street. Don't tempt fate. Keep calm. Check the stick. (A thin blue line, a background going browner.) I don't believe it. It's not true. Nothing's true. The snow is falling. It is. Gusts of it suddenly, the flakes very much bigger and whiter, heavy enough not to swirl so much now, but coming down straighter, falling, like snow should. If it falls like this for an hour, there will be enough for snowballs, for a snowman.

And so I sit and I wait and I watch the snow. It doesn't seem a long time, it doesn't seem like time at all, but like something light and flying and rising and full of joy, and also something to be hugged close. Simultaneously nothing matters and everything matters and still it snows.

Paul is first down at 7.30.

'Couldn't you sleep?' he says.

'No.'

'Did Sam wake?'

'No.'

He goes to the breadbin and extracts the wholemeal loaf, slicing it for toast. As he puts the bread under the grill he looks out of the window.

'Bet the bloody car won't start,' he remarks.

Why am I delaying? Why can't I tell him the news? Because the words 'I'm pregnant' won't come out of my mouth. Framing it, saying it seems too dangerous, too hubristic. Besides, what if it's not true?

'I did a pregnancy test', I say to his back. This is neutral, scientific, nothing to do with me. 'And it's positive.'

'I wouldn't set too much store by that,' he says, flipping the toast, not turning round.

'That's not quite the reaction I expected!' I burst out. Yet in the moment of my cry I see it is my reaction, it's disbelief.

There's a pause and then the snap of the grill button. For a moment Paul stares away from me, out of the window. Then he turns and begins to walk towards me, his mouth smiling such a smile as I haven't seen for two years. And the closer he gets the more beautiful he seems to me and I get up to greet him, to share the joy and the yearning I see in his eyes. And as I feel the first touch of his outstretched arms, I know that we may never have this child, that I may miscarry, but it doesn't matter, can't matter, because I have the arms of this precious man around me and he's holding me. Holding me. And I'm holding him.

At that moment Sam plummets into the room.

'It's snowing!' he shrieks.